The
Realm
of
Science

THE SUBSTANCE
OF OUR WORLD:
Earth, Water
and Air

VOLUME 16

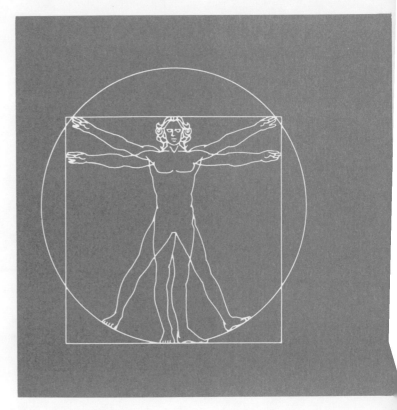

THE
REALM
OF
SCIENCE

DAVID ROSENBERG, *Director*

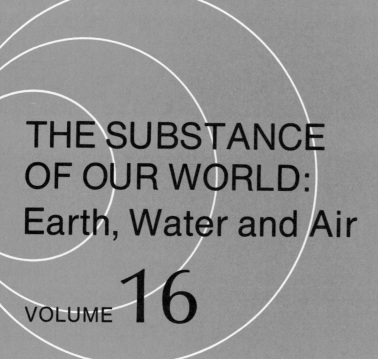

THE SUBSTANCE OF OUR WORLD: Earth, Water and Air

VOLUME 16

STANLEY B. BROWN   Editor-in-Chief

L. BARBARA BROWN   Associate Editor

SCIENTIFIC ADVISORY BOARD

TOUCHSTONE PUBLISHING COMPANY   *Louisville, Kentucky*

Science is the attempt
to make the chaotic diversity
of our sense experience
correspond to
a logically uniform system
of thought.

ALBERT EINSTEIN

THE REALM OF SCIENCE is divided into 5 parts, each covering a broad concept of science rather than a traditional discipline.

PART I   THE NATURE OF SCIENCE

VOLUME 1. The History and Spirit of Science
2. Traditions of Scientific Inquiry
3. Fundamentals of Mathematics
4. The Language of Science: Mathematics and the Physical Sciences

PART II   THE NATURE OF MATTER AND ENERGY

VOLUME 5. Discovering the Nature of Matter
6. The Dynamics of Being: Matter and Carbon Chemistry
7. Foundations of Physics: Mechanics and Optics in Classical Physics
8. The Evolving Knowledge: Further Developments in Classical Physics
9. Revolution in Science: Relativity, Quantum and Nuclear Physics
10. The New Science: Recent Advances in Physics

PART III THE NATURE OF SPACE

VOLUME 11. Atoms, Stars and Nebulae
12. Many Worlds: The Discovery of Galactic Systems
13. The Nature of the Universe: Modern Cosmology
14. Man and the Conquest of Space

PART IV   THE NATURE OF EARTH: ENVIRONMENT

VOLUME 15. The Earth and Its Origin
16. The Substance of Our World: Earth, Water and Air

PART V   THE NATURE OF LIFE

VOLUME 17. The Living World: Cells, Molecules and Metabolism
18. The Code of Life: Genetics and Development
19. The Continuum of Life: Structure, Classification and Evolution
20. Directions and Dimensions of Life: Ecology, Man and Nature

21. SCIENTHESIS

Copyright © 1972 by Touchstone Publishing Company
Printed in the United States of America
Library of Congress Catalog Card Number: 76-157124

CONTENTS

I   THE CYCLE OF CHANGE, *James Hutton*   10

II   THE MEANING OF SCENERY, *John A. Shimer*   20

III BURIED LANDSCAPES, *Harris B. Stewart, Jr.*   28

IV   "FATHER AIR," *George Gamow*   42

V   THE NATURE OF THE ATMOSPHERE, *Samuel Namowitz and Donald Stone*   47

VI   ATMOSPHERIC MOISTURE AND PRECIPITATION, *Vernor C. Finch,*
     Glenn T. Trewartha, Arthur H. Robinson and Edwin H. Hammond   54

VII STORMS, *Louis J. Battan*   73

VIII RADAR OBSERVES THE WEATHER, *Louis J. Battan*   79

IX   THE JET-STREAM, *Theo Loebsack*   83

X   KRAKATOA, *William C. Putnam*   89

XI   THE EARTH BENEATH THE SEA, *Francis P. Shepard*   95

XII OCEANOGRAPHY, *William S. von Arx*   112

XIII ON GEOLOGICAL AND ASTRONOMICAL BACKGROUNDS,
     William S. von Arx   115

XIV CHARACTERISTICS OF SEA WATER, *William S. von Arx*   130

XV   THE SCIENCE OF SUBSURFACE WATER, *Roger De Wiest*   145

XVI GROUND WATER, *John G. Ferris*   156

XVII DESERTS, *William C. Putnam*   171

     Index   185

CONSULTANTS
AND
CONTRIBUTORS

LAWRENCE H. BALTHASER
Department of Physical Sciences
California State Polytechnic College
San Luis Obispo, California

ROBERT BLAKELY
Indiana Geological Survey
Indiana University
Bloomington, Indiana

RICHARD BOOLOOTIAN
Department of Zoology
University of California
Los Angeles, California

JOSEPH C. BOONE
Department of Physical Sciences
California State Polytechnic College
San Luis Obispo, California

MARTIN S. BURKHEAD
Department of Astronomy
Indiana University
Bloomington, Indiana

LOUISE B. DUNN
Department of Anthropology
University of Utah
Salt Lake City, Utah

WILLIAM W. EIDSON
Department of Physics
University of Missouri at St. Louis
St. Louis, Missouri

LEO C. FAY
Department of Education
Indiana University
Bloomington, Indiana

DAVID W. HAFEMEISTER
Department of Physics
California State Polytechnic College
San Luis Obispo, California

CHARLES W. HAGEN, JR.
Department of Biology
Indiana University
Bloomington, Indiana

ELIZABETH O. HANSEN
Division of Science Education
University of California
Berkeley, California

JULIUS T. HANSEN
Department of Physiology
Medical School, St. Louis University
St. Louis, Missouri

VIRGIL HENISER
Coordinator for School Science
Indiana University
Bloomington, Indiana

CHRISTIAN E. KASLOW
Department of Chemistry
Indiana University
Bloomington, Indiana

BRUCE C. KETCHAM
Department of Aerospace, Office of Research
University of Tulsa
Tulsa, Oklahoma

PAUL E. KLINGE
Associate Dean, Research
Indiana University
Bloomington, Indiana

WENDELL F. McBURNEY
Science Coordinator
Indiana University
Bloomington, Indiana

LEO OLINER
Chief of Research in Endocrine
    and Metabolism
Veterans Administration Office
Washington, D. C.

THOMAS G. PERRY
Department of Geology
Indiana University
Bloomington, Indiana

JOHN RODGERS
Department of Philosophy
St. John's College
Santa Fe, New Mexico

JOHN H. RUGHEIMER
Department of Physics
Indiana University
Bloomington, Indiana

MILLARD SEELEY
Department of Chemistry
University of Arizona
Tuscon, Arizona

MAYNARD THOMPSON
Department of Mathematics
Indiana University
Bloomington, Indiana

JAMES A. WIXOM
Department of Mathematics
University of Utah
Salt Lake City, Utah

JANIS B. WIXOM
Churchill Junior High School
Salt Lake City, Utah

ARTHUR YOUNG
Department of Astronomy and Physics
San Diego State College
San Diego, California

EDITORIAL STAFF

Managing Editor: Richard E. Kirk
Senior Editor: Charlotte A. Jeanes
Coordinating Editor: Phyllis W. Kirk
Art Editor: Mary E. Holloway
Research Editor: Jean M. White
Contributing Editors: James N. Rogers
Frances L. Hackett
Editorial Assistants: Della A. Sarks
Joyce Walaszek
Peggy Patrick
Barbara Lind
Ruth Harley

ART STAFF

Art Director: Ben J. Sandman
Designer: Joseph Yurkas

CONTRIBUTING ARTISTS:
Eric Wehder Jr.
Ralph A. Welch
Fred DeCore
Robert W. Weston
Robert B. Dempley
David E. Barned
Raymond L. Eckerle
David R. Williams
Charles J. Bauer
Louis E. Givan
James E. Summers
Enoch Harned

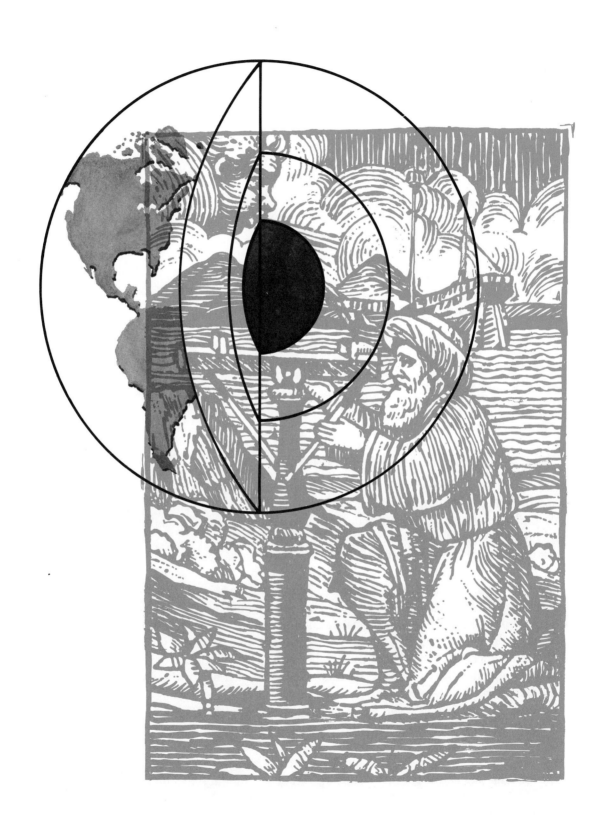

J AMES HUTTON WAS INTRODUCED in Volume 15 as the Founder of Geology. The following selection, written by James Hutton, presents his philosophy, as well as his theory of the earth, with a clarity that only his own words can convey.

Hutton's theory was simple, bold in conception, appealing in its suggestion, and based on a broad foundation of personal observation and reflection. When Hutton presented his views, he was accused of irreligious tendencies, and his keen interpretations of nature were for many years generally dismissed as irrelevant. While he accumulated a multitude of proofs suggesting an orderly design, or system, by which nature balances and maintains the livable condition of the earth, his doctrine involved acceptance of an unlimited span of time for the continual changes to have occurred.

When he died in 1797, the world at large had not yet accepted the notions resulting from his intensely scientific attitude, sincerity and genius. The following selection presents Hutton's brilliant insights and inferences, written in the humble but affirmative words of an outstanding pioneer of science generally and of geology in particular.

The Cycle of Change

From James Hutton, "Summary of the Doctrine which Has Been Now Illustrated," *Theory of the Earth* (Edinburgh, 1795), Part II, Chapter XIV.

THE SYSTEM of this earth appears to comprehend many different operations; and it exhibits various powers co-operating for the production of those effects which we perceive. Of this we are informed by studying natural appearances; and in this manner we are led to understand the nature of things, in knowing causes.

That our land, which is now above the level of the sea, had been formerly under water, is a fact for which there is everywhere the testimony of a multitude of observations. This indeed is a fact which is admitted upon all hands; it is a fact upon which the speculations of philosophers have been already much employed; but it is a fact still more important, in my opinion, than it has been ever yet considered. It is not, however, as a solitary fact that any rational system may be founded

upon this truth, that the earth had been formerly at the bottom of the sea; we must also see the nature and constitution of this earth as necessarily subsisting in continual change; and we must see the means employed by nature for constructing a continent of solid land in the fluid bosom of the deep. It is then that we may judge of that design, by finding ends and means contrived in wisdom, that is to say, properly adapted to each other.

We have now given a theory founded upon the actual state of this earth, and the appearances of things, so far as they are changing; and we have, in support of that theory, adduced the observations of scientific men, who have carefully examined nature and described things in a manner that is clear and intelligible. We are now to take a review of the principle points on which this theory hangs; and to endeavour to point out the importance of the subject, and the proper manner of judging with regard to a theory of the earth, how far it is conform to the general system of nature, which has for object a world sustaining plants and animals.

If it should be admitted, that this earth had been formed by the collection of materials deposited within the sea, there will then appear to be certain things which ought to be explained by a theory, before that theory be received as belonging to this earth. These are as follows:

First, We ought to show how it came about that this whole earth, or by far the greatest part in all the quarters of the globe, had been formed of transported materials collected together in the sea. It must be here remembered, that the highest of our mountainous countries are equally formed of those travelled materials as are the lowest of our plains; we are not therefore to have recourse to any thing that we see at present for the origin of those materials which actually compose the earth; and we must show from whence had come those travelled materials, manufactured by water, which were employed in composing the highest places of our land.

Secondly, We must explain how those loose and incoherent materials had been consolidated, as we find they are at present. We are not here to allow ourselves the liberty, which naturalists have assumed without the least foundation, of explaining every thing of this sort by *infiltration,* a term in this case expressing nothing but our ignorance.

Thirdly, The strata are not always equally consolidated. We often find contiguous strata in very different states with respect to solidity; and sometimes the most solid masses are found involved in the most porous substance. Some explanation surely would be expected for this appearance,

which is of a nature so conclusive as ought to attract the attention of a theorist.

Fourthly, It is not sufficient to show how the earth in general had been consolidated; we must also explain, how it comes to pass that the consolidated bodies are always broken and intersected by veins and fissures. In this case, the reason commonly given, that the earth exposed to the atmosphere had shrunk like moist clay, or contracted by the operation of drying, can only show that such naturalists have thought but little upon the subject. The effect in no shape or degree corresponds to that cause; and veins and fissures, in the solid bodies, are no less frequent under the level of the sea, than on the summits of our mountains.

Fifthly, Having found a cause for the fracture and separation of the solid masses, we must also tell from whence the matter with which those chasms are filled, matter which is foreign both to the earth and sea, had been introduced into the veins that intersect the strata. If we fail in this particular, What credit could be given to such hypotheses as are contrived for the explanation of more ambiguous appearances, even when those suppositions should appear most probable?

Sixthly, Supposing that hitherto every thing had been explained in the most satisfactory manner, the most important appearances of our earth still remain to be considered. We find those strata that were originally formed continuous in their substance, and horizontal in their position, now broken, bended, and inclined, in every manner and degree; we must give some reason in our theory for such a general changed state and disposition of things; and we must tell by what power this event, whether accidental or intended, had been brought about.

Lastly, Whatever powers had been employed in preparing land, while situated under water, or at the bottom of the sea, the most powerful operation yet remains to be explained; this is the means by which the lowest surface of the solid globe was made to be the highest upon the earth. Unless we can show a power of sufficient force, and placed in a proper situation for that purpose, our theory would go for nothing, among people who investigate the nature of things, and who, sounding on experience, reason by induction from effect to cause.

Nothing can be admitted as a theory of the earth which does not, in a satisfactory manner, give the efficient causes for all these effects already enumerated. For, as things are universally to be acknowledged in the earth, it is essential in a theory to explain those natural appearances.

But this is not all. We live in a world where order every where prevails, and where final causes are as well known, at least, as those which are efficient. The muscles, for example, by which I move my fingers when I write, are no more the efficient cause of that motion, than this motion is the final cause for which the muscles had been made. Thus, the circulation of the blood is the efficient cause of life; but, life is the final cause, not only for the circulation of the blood, but for the resolution of the globe: Without a central luminary, and a revolution of the planetary body, there could not have been a living creature upon the face of this earth; and, while we see a living system on this earth, we must acknowledge, that in the solar system we see a final cause.

Now, in a theory which considers this earth as placed in a system of things where ends are at least attained, if not contrived in wisdom, final causes must appear to be an object of consideration, as well as those which are efficient. A living world is evidently an object in the design of things, by whatever Being those things had been

designed, and however either wisdom or folly may appear in that design. Therefore the explanation, which is given of the different phenomena of the earth, must be consistent with the actual constitution of this earth as a living world, that is, a world maintaining a system of living animals and plants.

Not only are no powers to be employed that are not natural to the globe, no action to be admitted of except those of which we know the principle, and no extraordinary events to be alledged in order to explain a common appearance, the powers of nature are not to be employed in order to destroy the very object of those powers; we are not to make nature act in violation to that order which we actually observe, and in subversion of that end which is to be perceived in the system of created things. In whatever manner, therefore, we are to employ the great agents, fire and water, for producing those things which appear, it ought to be in such a way as is consistent with the propagation of plants and life of animals upon the surface of the earth. Chaos and confusion are not to be introduced into the order of nature, because certain things appear to our partial views as being in some disorder. Nor are we to proceed in feigning causes, when those seem insufficient which occur in our experience.

Animal life being thus considered as an object in the view of nature, we are to consider this earth as being the means appointed for that end; and then the question is suggested, How far wisdom may appear in the constitution of this earth, as being *means* properly adapted to the system of animal life, which is evidently the end. This is taking for granted, that there is a known system of the earth which is to be tried—how far properly adapted to the end intended in nature. But, it is this very system of the earth which is here the subject of investigation; and, it is in order to discover the *true system* that we are to examine, by means of final causes, every theory which pretends to show the nature of that system, or to assign efficient causes to physical events.

Here then we have a rule to try the propriety of every operation which should be acknowledged as in the system of nature, or as belonging to the theory of this earth. It is not necessary that we should see the propriety of every natural operation; our natural ignorance precludes us from any title to form a judgment in things of which we are not properly informed; but, no suppositions of events, or explanations of natural appearances, are to be admitted into our Theory, if the propriety of those alledged operations is not made to appear. We are now to make an application.

This earth, which is now dry land, was under water, and was formed in the sea. Here is a matter of fact, and not of theory, so far as it can be made as evident as any thing of which we have not seen the immediate act or execution. But the propriety of this matter of fact is only to be perceived in making the following acknowledgment, That the origin of this earth is necessarily placed in the bottom of the sea. In supposing any other origin to this habitable earth, we would see the impropriety of having it covered with water, or drowned in the sea. But, being formed originally at the bottom of the sea, if we can explain the phenomena of this earth by natural causes, we will acknowledge the wisdom of those means, by which the earth, thus formed at the bottom of the sea, had been perfected in its nature, and made to fulfil the purpose of its intention, by being placed in the atmosphere.

If the habitable earth does not take its origin in the waters of the sea, the washing away of the matter of this earth into the sea would put a period to the existence of that system which forms the admirable constitution of this living world. But, if the origin of this earth is founded in the sea, the matter which is washed from our land is only proceeding in the order of the system; and thus no change would be made in the general system of this world, although this particular earth, which we possess at present, should in the course of nature disappear.

It has already been our business to show that the land is actually wasted universally, and carried away into the sea. Now, What is the final cause of this event?—Is it in order to destroy the system of this living world, that the operations of nature are thus disposed upon the surface of this earth? Or, Is it to perpetuate the progress of that system, which, in other respects, appears to be contrived with so much wisdom? Here are questions which a Theory of the Earth must solve; and here, indeed, must be found the most material part by far of any Theory of the Earth. For, as we are more immediately concerned with the operations of the surface, it is the revolutions of that surface which forms, for us, the most interesting subject of inquiry.

Thus we are led to inquire into the final cause of things, while we investigate an operation of such magnitude and importance, as is that of forming land of sea, and sea of land, of apparently reversing nature, and of destroying that which is so admirably adapted to its purpose. Was it the work of accident, or effect of an occasional transaction, that by which the sea had covered our land? Or, Was it the intention of that Mind which formed the matter of this globe, which endued that matter with its active and its passive powers, and which placed it with so much wisdom among a numberless collection of bodies, all moving in a system? If we admit the first, the consequence of such a supposition would be to attribute to chance the constitution of this world, in which the systems of life and sense, of reason and intellect, are necessarily maintained. If again we shall admit, that there is intention in the cause by which the present earth had been removed from the bottom of the sea, we may then inquire into the nature of that system in which a habitable earth, possessed of beauty, arranged in order, and preserved with economy, had been formed by the mixture and combination of the different elements, and made to rise out of the wreck of a former world.

In examining the structure of our earth, we find it no less evidently formed of loose and incoherent materials, than that those materials had been collected from different parts, and gathered together at the bottom of the sea. Consequently, if this continent of land, first collected in the sea, and then raised above its surface, is to remain a habitable earth, and to resist the moving waters of the globe, certain degrees of solidity or consolidation must be given to that collection of loose materials; and certain degrees of hardness must be given to bodies which were soft or incoherent, and consequently so extremely perishable in the situation where they now are placed.

But, at the same time that this earth must have solidity and hardness to resist the sudden changes which its moving fluids would occasion, it must be made subject to decay and waste upon the surface exposed to the atmosphere; for, such an earth as were made incapable of change, or not subject to decay, could not afford that fertile soil which is required in the system of this world, a soil on which depends the growth of plants and life of animals,—the end of its intention.

Now, we find this earth endued precisely with that degree of hardness and consolidation as qualifies it at the same time to be a fruitful earth, and to maintain its station with all the permanency compatible with the nature of things, which

are not formed to remain unchangeable.

Thus we have a view of the most perfect wisdom, in the contrivance of that constitution by which the earth is made to answer, in the best manner possible, the purpose of its intention, that is, to maintain and perpetuate a system of vegetation, or the various race of useful plants, and a system of living animals, which are in their turn subservient to a system still infinitely more important, I mean a system of intellect. Without fertility in the earth, many races of plants and animals would soon perish, or be extinct; and, without permanency in our land, it were impossible for the various tribes of plants and animals to be dispersed over all the surface of a changing earth. The fact is, that fertility, adequate to the various ends in view, is found in all the quarters of the world, or in every country of the earth, and, the permanency of our land is such, as to make it appear unalterable to mankind in general, and even to impose upon men of science, who have endeavoured to persuade us that this earth is not to change. Nothing but supreme power and wisdom could have reconciled those two opposite ends of intention, so as both to be equally pursued in the system of nature, and both so equally attained as to be imperceptible to common observation, and at the same time a proper object for the human understanding.

We thus are led to inquire into the efficient causes of this constitution of things, by which solidity and stability had been bestowed upon a mass of loose materials, and by which this solid earth, formed first at the bottom of the sea, had been placed in the atmosphere, where plants and animals find the necessary conditions of their life.

Now, we have shown, that subterraneous fire and heat had been employed in the consolidation of our earth, and in the erection of that consolidated body into the place of land. The prejudices of mankind, who cannot see the steps by which we come at this conclusion, are against the doctrine; but, prejudice must give way to evidence. No other Theory will in any degree explain appearances, while almost every appearance is easily explained by this Theory.

We do not dispute the chymical action and efficacy of water, or any other substance which is found among the materials collected at the bottom of the sea; we only mean to affirm, that every action of this kind is incapable of producing perfect solidity in the body of earth in that situation of things, whatever time should be allowed for that operation, and that whatever may have been the operations of water, aided by fire, and evaporated by heat, the various appearance of mineralization, (every where presented to us in the solid earth, and the most perfect objects of examination), are plainly inexplicable upon the principle of aqueous solution. On the other hand, the operation of heat, melting incoherent bodies, and introducing softness into rigid substances which are to be united, is not only a cause which is proper to explain the effects in question, but also appears, from a multitude of different circumstances, to have been actually exerted among the consolidated bodies of our earth, and in the mineral veins with which the solid bodies of the earth abound.

The doctrine, therefore, of our Theory is briefly this, That, whatever may have been the operation of dissolving water, and the chymical action of it upon the materials accumulated at the bottom of the sea, the general solidity of that mass of earth, and the placing of it in the atmosphere above the surface of the sea, has been the immediate operation of fire or heat melting and expanding bodies.

Here is a proposition which may be tried, in applying it to all the phenomena of the mineral region; so far as I have seen, it is perfectly verified in that application.

We have another proposition in our Theory; one which is still more interesting to consider. It is this, That as, in the mineral regions, the loose or incoherent materials of our land had been consolidated by the action of heat; so, upon the surface of this earth exposed to the fluid elements of air and water, there is a necessary principle of dissolution and decay, for that consolidated earth which from the mineral region is exposed to the day. The solid body being thus gradually impaired, there are moving powers continually employed, by which the summits of our land are constantly degraded, and the materials of this decaying surface travelled towards the coast. There are other powers which act upon the shore, by which the coast is necessarily impaired, and our land subjected to the perpetual incroachment of the ocean.

Here is a part of the Theory with which every appearance of the surface may be compared. I am confident that it will stand the test of the most rigid examination; and that nothing but the most inconsiderate judgment may mistake a few appearances, which, when properly understood, instead of forming any subject of objection to the Theory, will be found to afford it every reasonable support or confirmation.

We have now seen, that in every quarter of the globe, and in every climate of the earth, there is formed, by means of the decay of solid rocks, and by the transportation of those moveable materials, that beautiful system of mountains and valleys, of hills and plains, covered with growing plants, and inhabited by animals. We have seen, that, with this system of animal and vegetable economy, which depends on soil and climate, there is also a system of moving water, poured upon the surface of the earth, in the most beneficial manner possible for the use of vegetation, and the preservation of our soil; and that this water is gathered together again by running to the lowest place, in order to avoid accumulation of water upon the surface, which would be noxious.

It is in this manner that we first have streams or torrents, which only run in times of rain. But the rain-water absorbed into the earth is made to issue out in springs, which run perpetually, and which, gathering together as they run, form rivulets, watering valleys, and delighting the various inhabitants of this earth. The rivulets again are united in their turn, and form those rivers which overflow our plains, and which alternately bring permanent fertility and casual devastation to our land. Those rivers, augmenting in their volume as they unite, pour at last their mighty waters into the ocean; and thus is completed that circulation of wholesome fluids, which the earth requires in order to be a habitable world.

Our Theory further shows, that in the ocean there is a system of animals which have contributed so materially to the formation of our land. These animals are necessarily maintained by the vegetable provision, which is returned in the rivers to the sea, and which the land alone or principally produces. Thus we may perceive the mutual dependence upon each other of those two habitable worlds,—the fluid ocean and the fertile earth.

The land is formed in the sea, and in great part by inhabitants of that fluid world. But those animals, which form with their *exuviae* such a portion of the land, are maintained, like those upon the surface of the earth, by the produce of that land to which they formerly had contributed. Thus the vegetable matter, which is produced upon the surface of the earth in such abundance for the use of animals, and which, in such various shapes, is carried by the rivers into the sea, there sustains that living system which is daily employed to make materials for a future land.

Here is a compound system of things, forming together one whole living world; a world maintaining an almost endless diversity of plants and animals, by the disposition of its various parts, and by the circulation of its different kinds of matter. Now, we are to examine into the necessary consequence of this disposition of things, where the matter of this active world is perpetually moved, in that salutary circulation by which provision is so wisely made for the growth and prosperity of plants, and for the life and comfort of its various animals.

If, in examining this subject, we shall find that there is nothing in the system but what is necessary, that is, nothing in the means employed but what the importance of the end requires; if we shall find that the end is steadily pursued, and that there is no deficiency in the means which are employed; and if it shall be acknowledged that the end which is attained is not idle or insignificant, we then may draw this conclusion, That such a system is in perfect wisdom; and therefore that this system, so far as it is found corresponding properly with natural appearances, is the system of nature, and not the creature of imagination.

Let us then take a cursory view of this system of things, upon which we have proceeded in our theory, and upon which the constitution of this world seems to depend.

Our solid earth is every where wasted, where exposed to the day. The summits of the mountains are necessarily degraded. The solid and weighty materials of those mountains are every where urged through the valleys, by the force of running water. The soil, which is produced in the destruction of the solid earth, is gradually travelled by the moving water, but is constantly supplying vegetation with its necessary aid. This travelled soil is at last deposited upon the coast, where it forms most fertile countries. But the billows of the ocean agitate the loose materials upon the shore, and wear away the coast, with the endless repetitions of this act of power, or this imparted force. Thus the continent of our earth, sapped in its foundation, is carried away into the deep, and sunk again at the bottom of the sea, from whence it had originated.

We are thus led to see a circulation in the matter of this globe, and a system of beautiful economy in the works of nature. This earth, like the body of an animal, is wasted at the same time that it is repaired. It has a state of growth and augmentation; it has another state, which is that of diminution and decay. This world is thus destroyed in one part, but it is renewed in another; and the operations by which this world is thus constantly renewed, are as evident to the scientific eye, as are those in which it is necessarily destroyed. The marks of the internal fire, by which the rocks beneath the sea are hardened, and by which the land is produced above the surface of the sea, have nothing in them which is doubtful or ambiguous. The destroying operations again, though placed within the reach of our examination, and evident almost to every observer, are no more acknowledged by mankind, than is that system of renovation which philosophy alone discovers.

It is only in science that any question concerning the origin and end of things is formed; and it is in science only that the resolution of those questions is to be attained. The natural operations of this globe, by which the size and shape of our land are changed, are so slow as to be altogether imperceptible to men who are employed in pursuing the various occupations of life and literature. We must not ask the industrious inhabitant, for the end or origin of this earth: he sees the present, and he looks no farther into the works of time than his experience can supply his reason. We must not ask the statesman, who looks into the history of time past, for the rise and fall

of empires; he proceeds upon the idea of a stationary earth and most justly has respect to nothing but the influence of moral causes. It is in the philosophy of nature that the natural history of this earth is to be studied; and we must not allow ourselves ever to reason without proper data, or to fabricate a system of apparent wisdom in the folly of a hypothetical delusion.

When, to a scientific view of the subject, we join the proof which has been given, that in all the quarters of the globe, in every place upon the surface of the earth, there are the most undoubted marks of the continued progress of those operations which wear away and waste the land, both in its heighth and wideth, its elevation and extension, and that for a space of duration in which our measures of time are lost, we must sit down contented with this limitation of our retrospect, as well as prospect, and acknowledge, that it is in vain to seek for any computation of the time, during which the materials of this earth had been prepared in a preceding world, and collected at the bottom of a former sea.

The system of this earth will thus appear to comprehend many different operations, or it exhibits various powers co-operating for the production of those appearances which we properly understand in knowing causes. Thus, in order to understand the natural conformation of this country, or the particular shape of any other place upon the globe, it is not enough to see the effects of those powers which gradually waste and wear away the surface, we must also see how those powers affecting the surface operate, or by what principle they act.

Besides, seeing those powers which are employed in thus changing the surface of the earth, we must also observe how their force is naturally augmented with the declivity of the ground on which they operate. Neither is it sufficient to understand by what powers the surface is impaired, for, it may be asked, why in equal circumstances, one part is more impaired than another; this then leads to the examination of the mineral system, in which are determined the hardness and solidity, consequently, the permanency of those bodies of which our land is composed; and here are sources of indefinite variety.

In the system of the globe every thing must be consistent. The changing and destroying operations of the surface exposed to the sun and influences of the atmosphere, must correspond to those by which land is composed at the bottom of the sea; and the consolidating operations of the mineral region must correspond to those appearances which in the rocks, the veins, and solid stones, give such evident, such universal testimony of the power of fire, in bringing bodies into fusion, or introducing fluidity, the necessary prelude to solidity and concretion.

Those various powers of nature have thus been employed in the theory, to explain things which commonly appear; or rather, it is from things which universally appear that causes have been concluded, upon scientific principles, for those effects. A system is thus formed, in generalizing all those different effects, or in ascribing all those particular operations to a general end. This end, the subject of our understanding, is then to be considered as an object of design; and, in this design, we may perceive, either wisdom, so far as the ends and means are properly adapted, or benevolence, so far as that system is contrived for the benefit of beings who are capable of suffering pain and pleasure, and of judging good and evil.

But, in this physical dissertation, we are limited to consider the manner in which things present have been made to come to pass, and not to inquire concerning the moral end for which those things may have been calculated. . . .

II

GEOLOGY IS OFTEN CALLED "The People's Science" because its materials comprise the scenery which surrounds everyone. Mountains, valleys, rocks, and oceans—these are the subjects the geologist studies and they are the sources of his knowledge.

The study of astronomy requires a certain grasp of mathematics and access to a telescope. The biologist needs a powerful microscope to even see some of the organisms he examines, and the chemist needs a laboratory full of test tubes and accurate measuring devices. The geologist uses chiefly his eyes. The layman with a minimal knowledge of natural phenomena can read much of what the geologist writes, and share his pleasure in understanding the world he sees around him.

A sensitivity for scenic beauty is a subjective thing. John A. Shimer, author of the next selection, colorfully cites a number of familiar examples of diversified landscapes. He explains that a knowledge of certain fundamental geologic forces can increase anyone's depth of appreciation for beautiful landscapes through an awareness of the restless energies that continually mold the earth's crust. Written in nontechnical terms, the selection gives the reader an impression of the earth as an "ever-oscillating platform," restless and always changing.

The Meaning of Scenery

From John A. Shimer, *This Sculptured Earth* (New York: Columbia University Press, 1959), pp. 2-13. Reprinted by permission of the publisher.

SCENERY means many things to many people. Each part of this sculptured earth has its own characteristic flavor and its own special type of landscape, and each arouses unexpected and varied reactions in the observer.

A map of the United States tells us that the country is composed simply of plains and mountains and plateaus, all enclosed by an irregular shoreline. This is the bare outline. What actually exists is a landscape of practically unlimited diversity. Think of the smooth grass-covered, tawny hills of California, and compare them with the jagged gray peaks of the Tetons, with touches of snow still clinging to them even on the hottest summer days. Picture the myriad pinnacles of Bryce Canyon, glowing in early morning sunlight, and then call to mind the vast monochromatic expanses of the arid desert regions of Nevada. Or imagine the subtle tones of a green carpet of young wheat on the far-reaching plains of the Dakotas, and contrast them with the flaming fall colors of the maples on some intimate hillside in Vermont.

Landscapes are certainly many faceted, and our appreciation of them is generally subjective. A scene is compounded of various elements, the weather, the verdure, the earth itself, and our appreciation depends on how closely we may feel "in tune" with our surroundings at a given moment.

Mountains are the epitome of grandeur, expressive of the awesome power of nature. Among them, a person may perhaps lose most completely his sense of self-importance and acquire a feeling of relative insignificance. For many, such regions offer a challenge and give a wonderful feeling of release and freedom from earthly cares.

The low rolling hills of the eastern Plains States convey an air of quiet serenity. Here the seasons come and go in everlasting cycles, and we are conscious of the passing of time, but not perhaps of dramatic changes in the face of the land such as we can sometimes find elsewhere.

A visit to the seacoast is associated with the eternal activity of moving water. Lazy summer days spent in the hot sun on a warm beach, the tide slowly covering the

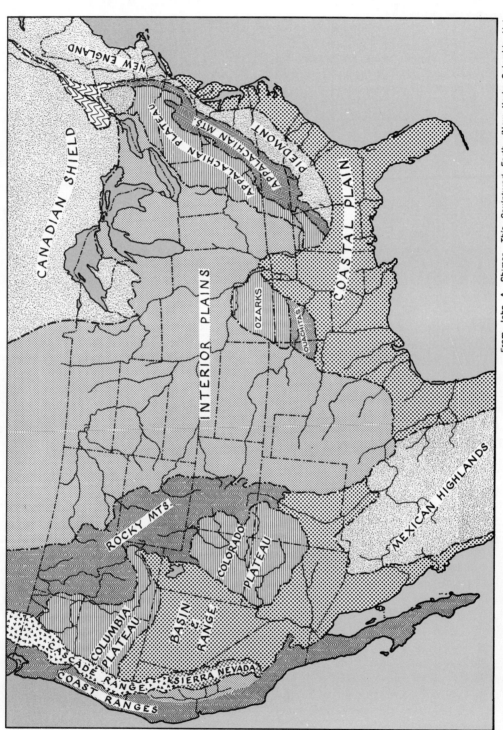

From John A. Shimer, *This Sculptured Earth,* (New York: Columbia University Press, 1959), pp. 6-7. By permission of Columbia University Press.

Geologic Provinces of the United States

land, contrast with times of strong wind and heavy surf.

An increased understanding of the various forces which have been important in molding our environment brings an even greater awareness and appreciation of our scenic heritage. Rather than decreasing our feeling of wonder such knowledge often intensifies our reaction. Also with increased understanding the seemingly haphazard arrangement of hills and valleys, plains and mountains, becomes less puzzling and we may even learn to recognize that the infinite number of scenic forms are really variants on a limited number of basic themes.

For a true appreciation of any landscape we must *see* and *understand* the varied shapes of hills and valleys as well as of the smaller scale ledges and slopes, and not be diverted by the manifold impressions created by vegetation, with its variety of shapes, colors, and odors, and the sounds and movement of running water, wind, and waves.

As seen from the air the landscape below us reveals arrangements of features which are difficult to perceive on land and which pose many questions for the traveler. For instance, on a flight from New York City to Quebec we see a striking number of lakes and swamps in an area with a surprising amount of forest cover, considering the large population of New England. In contrast, on a flight over the Appalachians from New York to Pittsburgh we notice a marked paucity of lakes and swamps. On such a flight we might also note a series of parallel forested ridges with intervening cultivated valleys somewhat to the west of Harrisburg, and farther west still nearer to Pittsburgh, an irregular land pattern, one of winding valleys and small irregular fields. In contrast, flying over the plains area of Iowa and Nebraska we see a network of large rectangular fields and straight roads extending to the horizon. Observations such as these

are sure to raise questions, many of which can be easily answered by a consideration of the various geological forces at work in the world.

The mountains of Death Valley and the arid areas of Nevada and Utah have a ragged tattered appearance. When we look down at such scenes we are at once aware that a great deal of material has been washed down from the mountains and spread out as alluvial fans in the intervening lower-lying places. It is clear that the ridges and pointed tops of the mountain ranges are residual features, left by the forces that have been carving the valleys. Here, we should probably not talk of hills rising above valleys but of valleys cut between hills. The relationship of hills and valleys is clearly evident in such an arid area. It is less obvious but equally true in the Appalachians and other mountainous areas where vegetation cloaks and obscures the details of the slopes.

The more we travel around the country and look at scenery, the more we become conscious of the worn, sculptured look of many parts of the land. A great deal of the world's scenery is obviously due to destruction. Solid rocks crumble on being exposed to the weather and are then carried away in this fragmental state, generally by running water, although the wind waves, glaciers, or underground water may in places be of paramount importance. We will find that this breakup and removal of rocks, the process of gradation, is active everywhere. It is one of the three major processes affecting the earth's crust.

With the continued attack of the forces of gradation the eventual removal of all mountains into the sea is inevitable. It has been estimated that if the present rate of weathering and erosion continues, the high parts of North America will be washed into the sea in less than twenty-five million years. We know that the earth is much

Spence Air Photos, Los Angeles

Death Valley, California. The rocks of the mountains have been weathered and the broken material washed into the intermontane basins. The watercourses are marked by salt deposits.

older than this. The implication is inevitable, therefore, that there must be some counterforces which cause the building up of land areas.

Diastrophism and igneous activity, the second and third major earth-shaping processes, together provide these necessary counterforces. They renew the high parts of the land, which the forces of gradation destroy bit by bit, thus creating as a by-product the great variety in the scenery of the world.

Igneous activity results in the growth of volcanoes and lava flows. Such features are very obvious at many places in the western part of the United States. The Cascade Mountains of Washington, Oregon, and northern California stand as monuments of the effectiveness of lava and ash in building up the land. The cinder cones

of Arizona in the San Francisco Mountain area are beautiful examples of landforms produced by somewhat smaller scale igneous activity. Sunset Crater as seen from the air is an unforgettable sight. It is a practically perfect cone with a small crater at the top; extending from its base there is a black irregularly shaped lava flow which stands out markedly against its lighter toned surroundings.

Evidence of the crustal instability associated with diastrophism is found everywhere in the world. At Pozzuoli on the coast of Italy, for example, the marble columns of the Greek temple of Serapis have small holes drilled in them, fifteen to twenty feet above the present level of the water. These holes were made by boring clams at a time when the columns were covered by the Mediterranean. They bear mute testimony to the drowning and partial reeleva-tion of this part of the world since ancient times.

The relationship between land and sea level has been an unstable one from very early times in earth history. Marine shells have been found in very odd places, away from their usual environment along the shore. Fossils of long extinct marine plants and animals are found in layers of lime-stone, shale, and sandstone, which are the solidified deposits of ancient sea beds, now located far from any present seacoast. Many of these former sea floors are now found at great elevations, in places thous-ands of feet above the present level of the ocean. During the attempt to scale Mount Everest in 1924, the geologist Noel E. Odell looked for and reported finding marine fos-sils embedded in sedimentary rock high up on the side of the mountain.

Sedimentary rock layers have often lost their original level position and are now crumpled and contorted. For instance, much of the mass of the Rocky Mountains is composed of such distorted material, orig-inally laid down when that part of North America was under the sea. Now these uplifted sediments are being removed by running water to form new beaches along other oceans. We can frequently see cross sections of some of these ancient tilted and uplifted sea beds as they lie exposed on canyon walls or cliff faces. In Glacier Park, Montana, lines made by such layers are easily noted on the steep slopes of many of the eroded peaks. And along the east margin of the Rockies in Colorado the up-turned edges of some of the more resistant sedimentary strata stand out as ridges flank-ing the mountain front. In the Garden of the Gods at Colorado Springs, the original-ly horizontal layers are now vertical and stand dramatically as red sandstone walls.

United States Department of the Interior—National Park Service Photo by Fred Mang, Jr.

Sunset Crater, Arizona. A cinder cone.

United States Department of the Interior—National Park Service Photo

Death Valley, California. Uplifted and tilted rock layers are visible on eroded mountain slopes.

Courtesy of Colorado Springs Chamber of Commerce

Garden of the Gods, Colorado. Rocks that were originally horizontal stand today as vertical walls.

Faulting or slipping along cracks in the crust may occur in places with the result that layers which were once continuous now stop abruptly and continue on the other side of the fault in an offset position. The result of such faulting can be seen especially clearly from the air, as, for example near Loveland, Colorado, where a number of hogback ridges are offset.

The great variety of distortions of the earth's crust is caused by apparently never-ending diastrophic activity, which raises or lowers crustal layers or tilts and crumples them in the process of mountain building.

The human life span is so short that the surface of the earth appears to be substantial. Scenes described long ago seem essentially the same today, and we feel sure will be so for many years to come. Of course, this is an illusion, at least from the geologist's point of view. When a geologist talks about hills which vanish and mountains which rise from the ocean he is obviously using time in terms different from those we commonly use; his time units are in thousands or millions of years. On the other hand, a geologist who deals with such a time scale gives great importance to little things which may seem insignificant to others. The washing of an unseeded lawn, the shifting of flagstones by frost action, and the breakup and decay of masonry are the results of exactly the same forces which in the long run can destroy the loftiest mountains. Viewed from the perspective of geologic time the surface of the earth is an ever-oscillating platform, where mountains rise and are washed away and where the sea floods first one part of the land, then another.

In a geological discussion of scenery it is important to appreciate that we are dealing with long periods of time, measured in millions of years, but how many millions in each case is of little importance. Actually it is more important to grasp the sequence of events which have occurred while realizing that we are dealing with time units which are really incomprehensible anyway.

IF MAN WERE ABLE TO VIEW the ocean floors as he does the surface of the continents, a whole new world of scenic beauty would be revealed to him. Vast mountain chains, deep elongated depressions, the flattest of plains, great volcanic mountains that from base to tip tower higher than Mount Everest and submarine canyons that equal the grandeur of the Grand Canyon of the Colorado—all lie hidden beneath the waters of the global sea.

Marine geology has as its purpose the exploration of approximately 72 percent of the earth's surface. Study of water movements, the terrain of the ocean floor, the sediments and the rocks that lie below are all within the realm of marine geology.

Harris B. Stewart, Jr., chief oceanographer for the U.S. Coast and Geodetic Survey, and chief scientist on the 1960 *Explorer* expedition, writes a colorfully descriptive account of the buried landscapes of the sea. He presents in nontechnical terms a concise survey of recent discoveries and methods of exploring on this relatively untouched frontier.

Buried Landscapes

THE PLEASANTLY undulating surface of the seas as seen from the promenade deck of a cruise ship gives not the slightest suggestion of the varied landscapes lying far beneath, buried by several miles of seawater. Not one whit more can be learned about these buried landscapes by looking out from the laboratory of an oceanographic survey ship. However, a ship of this type is outfitted with electronic devices for determining the shape of the bottom, so that the oceanographer has merely to stop watching the scenery and turn to watch the fathometer as it pings away relentlessly to produce a continuous trace of the sea floor directly beneath the moving ship.

This method involves bouncing a ping of sound off the ocean floor and measuring the time it takes to return to the ship. Previous to the development of this echo-sounding technique, the only knowledge of the shape of the sea floor was gained by the laborious—and none too accurate—method of lowering a weighted hemp line and later a thin wire from the ship and noting how much was needed to reach the bottom.

Needless to say, even after many years of such lowerings, the shape of the ocean basins was known only in the most general way, and the details were not known at all. It was really the development of the continuously recording echo sounder in the 1940's that opened up the buried landscapes to exploration for the first time. Utilizing this equipment, a ship could steam continuously from New York to Liverpool and on arrival unroll a long strip of paper on which was recorded an unbroken trace of the depth of the ocean along the entire track. Some version of this basic echo-sounding set is now standard equipment on every research and survey ship, and the precision survey recorders now being built enable the marine surveyor to obtain an expanded and detailed trace of the surface of the ocean bottom.

Such tracings, however, are of very limited value for mapping purposes unless the position of the ship is known at all times. It is of little use to know that there is a large undersea mountain somewhere between New York and Liverpool, unless you are able to pinpoint it on a chart. Although we now know a good deal about the undersea topography and have much of it generally located, it is only within the past few years that accurate long-range electronic navigation systems have been available so that a ship can know where it is with anything better than the two-to-five mile accuracy of the classic celestial navigation techniques.

Loran-C is such a system, but it is costly to maintain, the shipboard receivers are expensive, and only a relatively small portion of the northern ocean is currently covered by this system. (The Loran-C system consists of powerful transmitters on shore which send radio signals to the ship from several stations. On shipboard, the time of arrival of the various signals, which varies according to the ship's distance from each station, provides an accurate "fix" of the ship's position.) When satellite navigation becomes a reality, we will be able to make accurate charts anywhere at sea. This will be an era that oceanographers have long awaited.

Mapping the Buried Mountains

Over the years, we have learned a good deal about the lands beneath the sea. We have sounded the deep oceanic trenches that contain the deepest known parts of the ocean. We have found countless isolated undersea mountains and some spectacular undersea mountain ranges. We have also found vast stretches of plains and some undersea channels that appear to be much like river channels on land. We know of the continental shelves and slopes that border our continental land masses, and we know the shape of many of the steep-walled submarine canyons that have been cut back into these continental margins. These are what we have found, but how were they formed? As the land geologist maps the shape of the landforms and samples the

materials of which they are made in an effort to learn their origins and history, so too the marine geologist approaches the problem of learning the "why" and "how" of the buried landscapes his instruments reveal.

The problems of the marine geologist are considerably greater than those of his dry-land counterpart. He is unable to sit on the slope of an undersea hill and look out across the valleys and hills before him. He is unable to produce accurate maps from aerial photographs or decide where a critical rock or sediment sample should be collected and then walk over and pick it up. He must work above a topography he cannot see and obtain his samples by lowering pipes and buckets to collect his samples in what is really a hit-or-miss sort of way. His maps he can construct only by moving his ship back and forth above the bottom with his echo sounder turning out rolls of paper that must then be scaled and plotted on a chart and contour lines drawn to reproduce on paper the shape of the area he has been covering. It sounds like a long and arduous task, and in a way it is. But to those who make such things their business, there is a real thrill to sit at the front of a fathometer and "bring in a seamount," as we say. The problem would be quite analogous to mapping a mountain from a slow-moving dirigible flying at a constant altitude above the clouds that totally blanket the mountain, when the only instrument is an altimeter that gives a record of your height above the ground.

Aboard ship, sitting before the fathometer hour after hour, one becomes almost hypnotized as each swing of the stylus arm makes one more mark, extending by a fraction of an inch the trace representing the bottom of the sea. The sea floor has many bumps and small knolls, but to qualify as a seamount a rise must be at least 500 fathoms (3000 feet) above the surrounding topography. As the trace of the bottom begins each new rise, you wonder if this will be a big one. Oftentimes as the rise crests at something less than 500 fathoms, your curiosity is aroused; so after a hurried conference you turn the ship around and recross the feature on a parallel track but a mile or so away from the previous one. If you are lucky, you have turned in the right direction and now recross the sea-mount at a higher elevation than on your first track. This pattern continues until you have passed the peak. Since you have been recording the depth every minute or so during all of this tracking and have plot-ted the soundings along a track that has taken into account the various changes in ship's course, you now try to "hit the top"— to find the shallowest sounding. From your plot, you call the bridge and give them the heading that you feel will move the ship directly over the peak of the mountain. An ocean current may have been causing a continuous drift throughout this survey, but if you have run one or more crosslines, you should have a fair estimate of how much and in what direction you have had to ad-just your lines in order to have exactly the same depth at the one point where the two lines cross. This calculation gives an indi-cation of the rate of ship's drift, and if you have cranked this additional variable into your estimate of the right course to take to "hit the top," you will probably do fairly well.

After you have gone through this proce-dure once or twice, it becomes a real game. There are numerous patterns that can be used, and there are good basic patterns dic-tated by statistics and by the theory of search. Most of us still, I think, would rath-er "play it by ear," that is, decide at the end of each crossing which way to turn more by intuition than by any preconceived pattern. The trenches and canyons of the sea floor are normally surveyed with lines

spaced as closely as time and the accuracy of your navigational control will allow, but always the crosslines are necessary to cor-rect for any drift of the ship due to surface currents or wind.

Most of our information on the deep sea has come not from the work of single ocean-ographic ships, but rather from a compi-lation of the soundings made along the tracks of all oceanographic ships that have traversed a given area. Very little of this sounding has been done on a systematic basis. The Gulf of Alaska is one exception. As the survey ships of the U.S. Coast and Geodetic Survey have each year moved from their Pacific base at Seattle to the working grounds along the many thousands of miles of coastline of Alaska and the Aleu-tian Islands, each ship has moved along a different line. These lines have been care-fully laid out in advance as part of an over-all scheme to insure maximum coverage of the entire Gulf of Alaska. Holidays, as we call the unmapped areas between two adja-cent lines, are frequently split with another track during a subsequent season. Even though, as one wit pointed out, you now have two holidays where you previously had only one, you do have additional infor-mation on which to base your contouring of the shape of the bottom of the ocean.

But what have these surveys revealed? How much do we now know of the shape of the ocean bottom and of the processes that have moulded its features?

Oceanic Trenches

If the waters of the sea were removed, and we examined the earth from an orbit-ing satellite, without a doubt the most strik-ing features we would see would be the great oceanic trenches. Comparable fea-tures are totally unknown on land, but the Aleutian Trench off southern Alaska paral-leling the Aleutian Islands chain is deeper and broader than the Grand Canyon and would extend from Boston to San Francisco. The magnificent Tonga-Kermadec Trench lying northeast of New Zealand is shorter but deeper and can be partially visualized by imagining a trench seven times as deep as the Grand Canyon and extending from New York to Kansas City. The Research Vessel *Horizon* of the Scripps Institution of Oceanography working above this trench during Christmas week in 1952 measured a depth of just under 35,000 feet. Imagine, if you can, a hole in the ocean floor into which Mt. Everest could be upended and dropped, disappearing completely from sight and still leaving a mile of seawater above it when it came to rest at the bottom. Such is the Tonga Trench.

The long, deep trenches are found only in the Pacific—if we can, for the sake of the discussion, consider the Java Trench as be-

ing along the margin of the Pacific. Their locations are shown in figure 1. In addition to the Aleutian and the Tonga-Kermadec trenches, there is the Peru-Chile Trench lying close along the west coast of South America, where the drop from the crest of the nearby Andes to the bottom of the coastal trench is over 40,000 feet. Off Central America is the Acapulco-Guatemala Trench, but aside from this and the short depression near Cedros Island off the west coast of Baja California, Mexico, there is no great deep off the west coast of North America south of the Aleutian Trench. From there, the string of trenches is almost continuous around a third of the rim of the Pacific, with the Kurile-Kamchatka Trench, the Japan and Nansei Shoto trenches, and the Mariannas Trench, where the Bathyscaph *Trieste* with two men aboard went

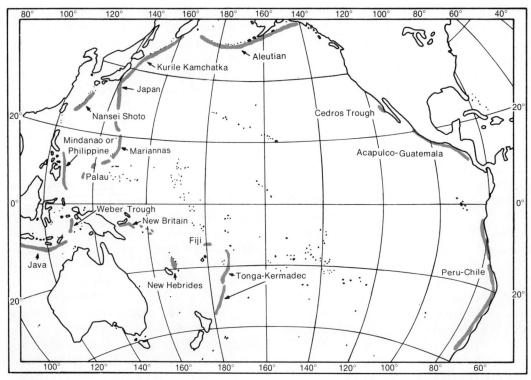

Figure 1 *Trenches of the Pacific.*

all the way to the bottom of 35,800 feet. The small Palau Trench is apparently a continuation of the Mariannas trend, and the Philippine, or Mindanao, Trench lies just east of the southern Philippine Islands.

The arc of trenches appears to split into two arms south of the Philippines, one swinging south and west through the so-called Weber Trough south of western New Guinea, into the deeps off Timor and Flores, and on into the Java Trench that swings westward along the southern side of the island of Java. The other arm is considerably less continuous, but the trend of the New Britain Trench off northeastern New Guinea appears to continue into the New Hebrides Trench and possibly into the small trench recently discovered by the Soviet ship *Vityaz* north of the Fiji Islands. East of these is the great Tonga-Kermadec Trench, but no trench has yet been found across the broad southern stretches of the Pacific between there and the Peru-Chile Trench. Thus the ring of trenches is more of a horseshoe than a true ring. Very probably these trenches are limited to the Pacific margins, and none exists in the vast relatively unexplored reaches of the Pacific south of about 30° south latitude. This southern area between New Zealand and South America is the least known of the major portions of the global sea, so it cannot yet be said with certainty that no trenches exist there.

The deepest parts of the global sea are in these oceanic trenches. If past history is any indication, we have not yet found the deepest part of the ocean, for there is a steady succession of new "maximum depth" reports. For a number of years, the deepest known place in the ocean was the Mindanao Deep off the Philippines. Then, as exploration covered more of these trenches, it was found that the Mariannas Trench off the island of Guam was deeper. The most recent maximum depth reported for this trench is the 1959 depth of 36,204 feet reported by the Soviet ship *Vityaz* southwest of the island of Guam (at 11°21′N,142° 12′E). For several years this remained the greatest known depth in the ocean. Then in the fall of 1962 the British survey ship *H.M.S. Cook*, while attempting to collect deep water samples in the Mindanao Trench, obtained a sounding of 37,782 feet east of the southern tip of the island of Mindanao in the Philippines (at 6°6′N, 127° 25′E). Such deep soundings must have various corrections applied to them, and the data must be accurately checked before the sounding can be considered as a true depth, but it is quite probable that the official record will move from the Mariannas Trench back to the Mindanao Trench. The southern hemisphere record has been held by the U.S. research vessel *Horizon* since 1952, when she obtained a depth of 34,884 feet in the Tonga Trench. Probably deeper depths exist. It is just a matter of time before they are found.

ORIGIN OF OCEANIC TRENCHES

The positions of the known trenches coincide very closely with the zones of the earth's most violent and concentrated earthquake activity. Nearly all the earthquakes of deep origin occur within the areas of the oceanic trenches. The ring of active volcanoes, the so-called "ring of fire," around the margins of the Pacific also coincides with these trench areas. Geologists feel that this is more than mere coincidence and that the active volcanoes, deep-focus earthquakes, and deep oceanic trenches are all somehow interrelated. The nature of the interrelationship is still in the realm of speculation, but it is just such speculation, such detective work on the global scale, that is part of the challenge of present-day marine geology.

Most probably the forces that produce the trenches are even now in action. The deep earthquakes might represent the release of tension built up by these great forces deep within the earth, and the volcanic activity would thus result from the reopening of old fissures and the occasional development of new ones through which the deeper molten material can escape to the surface. But what are these "forces" that cause all of this changing of the earth's shape? We really do not know, but we amass as many facts as we can, come up with a hypothesis that appears to explain the known facts, and then decide what additional facts we need in order to prove or disprove the original explanation. As new discoveries provide data that somehow do not fit the existing explanation, the original hypothesis must be modified. By the same token, there is the occasional thrill of discovering new facts that fit exactly the hypothesis currently in vogue.

The work on the Pacific trenches is a case in point. Current thinking is that these great trenches represent areas where the crust of the earth is actually being pulled down into the deeper, less rigid portion of the earth. This may seem like a fantastic idea at first, but consider the kitchen analogy of a large pan of water sitting across two burners on a stove, with each end of the pan resting over a burner. The warmed water at the ends will rise as it is heated, and the cooler water will descend in the middle until two vertical cells of moving water are formed. Surface currents are then moving from the ends of the pan across the top to the middle, where they meet and descend. Now assume that you cover the surface of the water with a layer of flour representing the crust of the earth. There will be a definite tendency for the flour in the middle to move downward where the two currents moving in from the ends meet and move downward. There will be a constant frictional force tending to pull the flour down in the middle. This force will be concentrated along the line where the tops of these two vertically moving cells meet, and there will be a continuous downward pull on the flour along this line and only along this line. This reasoning, when applied to the earth, does explain how the trenches might be pulled down, but it also requires that there be large vertical convection cells actively operating within the less rigid portion of the earth beneath the crust.

This was a new and an almost incredible idea when it was first proposed, but if it were true it would explain the origin of the great trenches. Then there was developed an ingenious piece of equipment called a heat probe. Lowered from a ship, this heavy probe penetrates the bottom of the ocean and measures and records the flow of heat upward from the sea floor into the overlying water. The obvious place to try out such an instrument was in a deep trench and on the relatively shallow rises well seaward of the trench. It is well known that in oil wells the temperature increases with depth as the warmer center of the earth is approached. Intuitively then, one would think that there would be higher temperatures encountered in the ocean floor at the bottom of a trench, which is several miles nearer the center of the earth, than would be found in the bottom on the more shallow rises far from the trenches. However, if the pan-on-the-stove idea, the convection cell hypothesis, were true, then you would expect that the warmer material would be rising to the surface under the shallower rises to give high heat-flow values, and the cooler material would be descending where the trenches were being pulled down and less heat flow would be found there.

The first lowerings in the Acapulco Trench and on the rise to seaward did show less heat-flow through the bottom of the trench. But these marine geologists are cautious. It could have been, they said, merely a difference in heat flow related to the fact that the measurements were made in two widely separated locations and not at all related to the trench and rise. It would take many more measurements before they could be sure. Over several years and several expeditions, the number of measurements of heat flow through the sea bottom has increased to the point where we are now sure that there is less upward flux of heat through the trenches. The Acapulco Trench, for example, has an upward loss of heat through its bottom which is less than half of the average for the surface of the earth. So in this case, the addition of new facts supported the hypothesis that their collection was designed to test, and the pan-on-the-stove or convection cell hypothesis is still the popular one used to explain the origin of these almost unbelievably large gashes in the bottom of the sea.

Mid-Ocean Rises

Undoubtedly, the oceanic trenches are closely related to the overall structural pattern of the earth as a geological unit, but we are just beginning to reach the stage where we have sufficient information even to recognize large-scale features in the earth's structure beneath the sea. As little as five years ago, the Mid-Atlantic Ridge running from Greenland to Antarctica and forming the backbone of the Atlantic was thought to be an isolated feature. Recent work, however, particularly by the marine geologists at the Lamont Geological Observatory of Columbia University, has shown that this is merely the Atlantic portion of a great continuous circumglobal range of mountains over 40,000 miles in length. The ridge extends into the Indian Ocean and through the eastern Pacific, actually "coming ashore" as part of the coastal mountain complex of western North America. Over part of the length of this ridge,

crossings with echo sounders have revealed a narrow median valley or rift, so this is a long mountain chain of global extent with a narrow valley running along the crest for at least some of its length.

In other crossings, there has been found a series of parallel ridges and rifts rather than just one major rift, and in still other crossings no depression at all has been found. Speculation is rife as to the cause of a feature of such magnitude. One hypothesis suggests that the earth is expanding and that this ridge-and-rift complex reflects the tensions resulting from this expansion. It is still much too early for anything other than the wildest of speculations, for additional work has shown that various segments of the worldwide chain of mountains have differing characteristics. Much of the chain still needs to be covered with reconnaissance surveys; none of it has been surveyed in accurate detail. Heat flow and gravity measurements are much too few, and few actual rock samples are as yet available for laboratory analysis and study. The discovery of this global mountain chain —or rather the discovery that the numerous previously known individual ridge systems were all part of the same worldwide system —is probably the most exciting discovery about our earth in the past twenty years. But this is a period of discovery in the global sea, and there have been other discoveries that will necessitate the rewriting of the classic texts in geology.

Fracture Zones

Work of marine geologists at the Scripps Institution of Oceanography has shown that running essentially east-west across the floor of the eastern Pacific is a series of great cracks in the sea floor, which have been called fracture zones. All discovered since World War II, five of the nine now known to exist have been found within the past seven years. A typical fracture zone is more than 1000 miles in length and about 100 miles wide. Lateral and vertical movement along cracks, or faults, within these zones has resulted in long east-west valleys and troughs, and up through these fissures have poured the lavas to make some spectacularly large undersea volcanoes. Typical vertical relief in these fracture zones shows differences of 10,000 feet between the tops and the bottoms of the ridges and valleys. The depth of the general ocean floor on opposite sides of the Pacific fracture zones often differs considerably, and the implication is that there has been a relative vertical movement of a whole segment of the ocean floor on one side of the zone.

Studies of the magnetic field across these features off California have provided information that is more than suggestive that large displacements of great blocks of the ocean floor have also taken place in the horizontal direction. The extent of these movements is amazingly large. The Mendocino fault, for example, is a prominent portion of one of these fracture zones. The magnetic evidence indicates very strongly that along 40° north latitude seaward of Cape Mendocino, California, the whole bottom of the ocean north of this fault has moved 750 miles to the west in relation to the area south of the fault. In the Atlantic, surveys are still too sparse to delineate comparable fracture zones—if they exist there at all. However, recent work by the Lamont Geological Observatory suggests that there has been some lateral movement along the ocean bottom seaward of the tip of Long Island. Perhaps, on further examination, this lateral movement will prove to be part of a fracture zone similar to those known from the Pacific, but we need more surveys of the sea floor, more information on which we can base and then test new hypotheses of the origin of our earth and the forces that have shaped its land and seascapes. We are just on the threshold of a new era of

global geological theories, and it appears that the real clues lie in the structures to be found at the bottom of the global sea.

Seamounts

Many of the smaller structural features of the deep sea are no less intriguing. The undersea mountains, or seamounts, hold a special fascination for the marine geologist. They have been found in all major branches of the global sea. Those crowding the crest of the Mid-Atlantic Ridge probably make up the greatest concentration in the Atlantic, but there is a fine string of seamounts between Cape Cod and Bermuda, and a recently published physiographic diagram of the Atlantic floor shows literally hundreds of these isolated peaks. Most of these undersea mountains appear to be volcanic in origin, that is, they are underwater volcanoes that now are dormant. Only rarely have these features been observed in the process of construction. Miojin Sho off the Japanese islands was one such undersea feature where an eruption was observed and photographed. The holocaust is well documented, but the price was high, for the entire scientific party and crew of the Japanese research vessel *Kaijo Maru* were lost when the ship was completely destroyed by a sudden eruption directly beneath it.

Obviously, some of these volcanoes have risen through the surface of the sea to become islands. The Hawaiian Islands are examples. Others have risen above the sea and then been reduced by the rasp file of the surf beating against their edges, to disappear again below the surface of the sea. Falcon Bank (formerly Falcon Island) in the Tonga Islands north of New Zealand is a classic example of this. Falcon Island has risen from beneath the sea and been cut back to sea level several times during the last two hundred years. When it was visited by the *Capricorn* Expedition of the

Scripps Institution of Oceanography in 1953, it was again totally submerged, and corals had started anew to grow on the pile of cinder rubble.

This same process of erosion to sea level is the best possible explanation for the many flat-topped seamounts that have been discovered throughout the Pacific. First explored in detail by a Princeton geology professor who found himself as the navigation officer on a Navy ship in the Pacific during World War II, the features were promptly named "guyots" by him in honor of the eminent Swiss geologist, Arnold Guyot, who was long a leading teacher with the Princeton Geology Department. These flat-topped seamounts, or guyots, in general have the shape of a truncated cone, an almost perfect volcano shape but with the top neatly sliced off. These are not volcanoes that have "blown their top," as did the one in which Crater Lake now sits, for there is no crater on the top of any known guyot. In most cases, guyots are as flat as a football field, perhaps with a narrow, gently sloping outer edge between the flat top and the steeply sloping sides. Planation to sea level by wave action was the obvious explanation, but most of these flat tops are now several hundred fathoms below sea level. The question immediately posed is "If the tops were made flat at sea level, how did they become 'drowned' so far below the present level of the sea surface?"

A rise in sea level may have contributed to their submergence, but more probably the major factor was the depression of the sea floor by the weight of the seamounts themselves and by what the geologists call regional downwarping. Echo-sounding surveys have revealed that many of these large seamounts are surrounded by a moat-like depression, suggesting that the sea floor just was unable to support all that weight of volcanic rock. That downwarping of the ocean bottom also can contribute

to the submergence of guyots is dramatically pointed out by a large flat-topped seamount just south of Kodiak, Alaska. The top of this guyot lies at more than 1000 fathoms (6000 feet) below the surface, considerably deeper than any of the many other guyots found in the North Pacific. The interesting fact here is that this is the only guyot found within the great Aleutian Trench. The implication is obvious that the seamount was carried downward by the downward movement of the trench itself, thus placing the top of this seamount well below the tops of all the others. This, incidentally, is additional evidence that the trenches are "pulled down" into the earth rather than having been cut as some might suppose.

Coral Islands

In the tropical areas where reef-building corals can flourish (between about 30° north and 30° south of the Equator), these flat-topped seamounts, while still relatively shallow, provided some of the platforms on which reefs became established. As the platforms subsided, upward growth of the reef progressed at a rate that kept the reef-building organisms within the sunlit depths where they could maintain reef growth. This mechanism may explain the development of some coral atolls such as Bikini and Eniwetok; but for others there is no known guyot beneath, and the Darwinian explanation of the upward growth of coral around the periphery of a sinking island appears to be the best explanation. Elsewhere, as at Falcon Bank, corals are known to become established on a submerged bank with no actual subsidence of the platform needed. In some other cases, there may have been no actual subsidence of the platform, but the organisms maintained upward growth as sea level rose.

The origin of atolls and other coral islands has been one of the great controversies of modern science. The four "D's"—Darwin, Dana, Davis, and Daly—made major contributions to the theory of the origin of coral islands, and the exploration of these intriguing features continues. Most probably it will be found that no sweeping theory can adequately explain all the atolls and other coral islands, but that each must be investigated separately to establish the method of its development. When many of these have been so studied, then we can begin to generalize.

Continental Shelf and Slope

Almost universally, the continents are bordered by a relatively shallow underwater terrace. The generally broad gently sloping landward portion is the *continental shelf.* The narrow, steeper outer slope where the terrace drops off to meet the deep sea floor is the *continental slope.* Coastal shipping is carried out over the continental shelf; in some areas petroleum is obtained from the ancient sediments below the surface of the shelf; much of the world's fishing is in the waters over the shelf; and the continental shelf will probably be the first area where commercial mineral recovery from the sea floor will be attempted. The continental shelf is the transition zone between the land and the deep sea, but even though it is the most available part of the global sea, only the inner portions of a relatively small part of it are adequately mapped.

On a world basis, the continental shelf averages a bit over 40 miles in width, with the average depth at the outer edge being about 70 fathoms (420 feet). The average slope from the shore to the outer edge is about ten feet per mile, being somewhat steeper on the inner than on the outer portions. The continental slope, on the other hand, though everywhere steeper than the gently sloping continental shelf, averages only about 400 feet per mile. Off southern

Cuba, along what appears to be a straight fault coast, the continental slope in places is steeper than 45°, but this is the extreme exception. Actually, this is probably the steepest underwater slope of any large extent anywhere in the sea.

The origin of the continental shelf and slope is still unknown. At first, before they had been surveyed or sampled to any extent, the continental terraces were thought to be a large apron of sediments washed into the ocean from the land and built up over the ages much the same way the delta of a river is built up. This view led to the conclusion that if you sampled the sediments on the surface of this terrace, you would find the coarser sediments nearer the land, and successively lighter sediments would have been carried successively farther to sea, so that on the very outer edge there would be nothing but fine muds. This all made very good sense until oceanographers began to sample the shelf sediments. As has so often been the case in the study of the sea, the pat explanations dreamed up from the comfort of a couch ashore crumble like a child's sand castle on a rising tide once you leave the couch and go out to see what actually is there.

So it was with the early explanations of the origin of the continental shelf and slope. Not only did the sediments not prove to be coarse inshore and finer offshore, but the reverse was true in many areas. In others there was a most patchy distribution of fine and coarse sediments, and in many places actual outcrops of rock were found at the very outer edge of the continental shelf. Perhaps, one might suppose, these shelves were planed off by surf action the way the guyots were. However, the use of explosives to study the subsurface structure by bouncing sound waves off layers of hard rock beneath the surface of the bottom has shown that, at least off the Atlantic coast of the United States, there is a deep fill of sediments on the landward part of the shelf. Certainly this is not what would be found if the terrace were a feature due to erosion rather than to filling by sediments. Most probably the explanation is not the same for the shelf everywhere in the world. In some cases—particularly off glaciated coasts—erosion may be the main agent of shelf formation. Elsewhere, as off large river mouths, sedimentation may be the dominant agent. Probably a combination of the two processes, erosion and deposition, will in the end be the best explanation; but in the meantime, this feature is "free game" for anyone who wants to take all the available facts into account and come up with a hypothesis of his own.

Submarine Canyons

Cutting through the continental slope and back into the continental shelf are many truly spectacular submarine canyons. Speculation on their origin has been a major controversial topic in marine geology for several decades, and countless professional papers advocating one hypothesis over another have been published in the scientific literature. The fight still rages, even though the earlier ideas of submarine solution as in limestone caverns, scouring by undertows, erosion by artesian springs, and gouging by seismic sea waves ("tidal waves") have been pretty well discarded by all marine geologists.

The controversy now revolves around two diametrically opposed concepts. The first is that the submarine canyons are of primarily submarine origin, having been carved under water by fast moving sediment-laden currents (the so-called turbidity currents). The other concept is that the canyons were basically formed above water at the time of a lower stand of sea level and are therefore essentially drowned land canyons. The facts marshalled by the proponents of each of these concepts are impres-

sive, so impressive in fact that they are probably both partly correct, and the real answer undoubtedly lies somewhere in between. According to this intermediate view, the canyons originated at a lower stand of the sea as land canyons. As sea level rose, however, the only canyons that remained were those that were not subsequently filled with sediment, but were kept open and deepened by turbidity current action. This hypothesis is just as open to argument as are the others based on the same facts.

The origin of submarine canyons is another of the "free game" areas, a grand submarine geological squabble in which all who have the facts are urged to take part. New exploratory tools such as the deep-sea cameras, the newly developed equipment for determining the thickness of sediments over the basement rock, and self-contained diving apparatus are all capable of shedding new light on this old problem. Any day a wholly new concept may have to be developed to explain an entirely new set of facts derived from the further study of these canyons.

Regardless of how they were formed, the canyons themselves are most interesting. Seaward of the Hudson River, the Hudson Canyon swings southeast across the continental shelf and slope and has been traced 200 miles seaward of the base of the continental slope by the Woods Hole Oceanographic Institution's research vessel *Atlantis*. On the shelf, the canyon is steep-sided and quite similar to land canyons. Below the base of the slope, the shape is more that of an entrenched river meandering across the sea floor.

On the west coast of the United States, the Monterey Submarine Canyon is the most spectacular. Its head is just off the end of the pier at Moss Landing near Monterey, California. The canyon is quite similar in profile to the Grand Canyon, and over part of its length is over a mile deep from the lip to the bottom. The canyon winds seaward for 50 miles, whereupon the steep inner canyon gives way to a broader trough that terminates in a wide fan-shaped submarine delta. Across this delta, several channels with levee-like sides show a marked similarity to those of river deltas on land. The leveed sides of the channels, undoubtedly formed by overflow as are the better-known natural levees of the Mississippi River, are strong evidence for the action of turbidity currents. These sediment-laden currents moving out of the canyon mouth and across the delta have mixed with the surrounding water, and some of the sediment thus lost from the major stream of turbid water has been deposited along the sides as levees. Undoubtedly these coastal canyons act as great sewers to carry seaward sediment that is moved into their shallower heads by longshore currents.

Detailed charts prepared by the U.S. Coast and Geodetic Survey have been carefully contoured and used to estimate the volume of the sediment in the delta at the mouths of several of the California canyons. From these charts it was found that there is many times more sediment in the deltas than ever was removed in the mere cutting of the canyons themselves. This sewer action must provide vast quantities of the finer sediments that do not end up on the deltas, but are carried far seaward in suspension and added to the sediments of the sea floor at great distances from their point of origin.

Many canyons head offshore opposite the mouths of rivers; but just enough do not, so that we cannot generalize. Most canyons appear to be cut into relatively soft sediments; but just enough are cut into hard rock (Carmel Canyon off California is cut into granite), so that again generalization is not warranted. The one thing all submarine canyons have in common is an air of mystery, that same challenge of the unexplored and unexplained. Diving in the head of Scripps Canyon off La Jolla, California, at a depth of 100 feet, you can reach out both hands and touch the walls on either side of the steep, narrow gorge. Looking upward, you see the narrow slit far above that is the surface, and between you and the sunlit surface of the sea myriads of fish drift lazily as black silhouettes. It is indeed a fascinating world.

The Shore

To landbound man, the most significant part of the ocean floor is the narrow line where the bottom of the sea becomes the surface of the land—the shore. Here he comes for his holidays to sun on the beach and to swim, to launch his boats, to fish, or just to sit and marvel at the ever-changing patterns of sea and sky. Here also is where he locates his great ports, docks his ships, and builds his marinas and resort hotels. But here too is where he releases much of his sewage and industrial wastes, where he struggles to keep the sands from moving out and leaving his structures to collapse into the sea, or struggles to keep the sand from moving in and filling his navigable channels. The shore is an area of almost constant change due both to the catastrophic and to the less violent day-to-day processes that mold and shape the shorelines of the world. As man builds new structures along the shore and interrupts the natural processes in action there, the delicate equilibrium is changed, and erosion or deposition takes place as the attempt is made to establish a new set of equilibrium conditions. It is an area of constant change, but by the same token, one of continuing interest to the marine geologist.

How many times have people come to the beach in the early spring and commented on all the rocks that "came in" during the winter? On many of the world's sand beaches, the last swimmer of the summer leaves a beach piled high with clean sand only to return in the spring to find the surface covered with coarse cobbles. Were he to keep weekly records of the height of the sand against a seawall or an abandoned piling, he would discover that instead of the rocks "coming in," the sand has gone out and uncovered the cobbles that lay beneath.

The annual migration of beach sand on and off the shore has been well documented. The high waves resulting from the storms of the northern-hemisphere winters rush high on the beaches, put the sand in suspension, and carry it seaward with the violent backwash. This action continues until the storm-generated surf of the winter is replaced by the more gentle waves of the summer period. Under these new conditions, the sand in suspension is carried up onto the beach, but the more gentle waves have no violent backwash. Rather, they sink into the porous beach and leave their suspended sand as a new layer upon the surface. This replenishment of sand continues throughout the summer until the cobbles are covered and the beach is back up to its autumn level.

Of course, there are other cycles that affect the beach, cycles related to regular tidal variations in sea level, but these are considerably less than the annual cycle. One storm in the middle of the summer, however, can upset the whole balance by moving out within a few days large quantities of sand that the remaining months of summer are unable to replace.

There is nothing sacred about the present level of the sea. There are marine deposits laid down on ancient sea bottoms now left high and dry by a retreating sea and found over much of the earth. Sea level has also stood much lower in the past, as attested to by ancient shoreline features now found buried under hundreds of feet of seawater. Our shorelines today are transient things, and future generations will do their bathing and their ship launching along a shore far inland or far seaward of the present shoreline. The change is gradual and may be heralded by the occasional storm surges that bury low-lying coastal airports under several feet of water or flood out the New York City subway system. On the other hand, the change may first be signaled by a gradual but continued shoaling of the major harbors, necessitating increased dredging to maintain the waterways. The one thing of which we are most sure is that it will change. The questions that cannot be answered yet are when will it become a significant factor in our coastal life and which way will sea level be going then, up or down?

Nearly three quarters of the earth's landscape is buried beneath the waters of the global sea. Some of the features of these buried landscapes are almost impossible for landbound man to visualize. Even as they are shown on the laboriously constructed maps of the sea bottom, the landscapes generate more questions than they answer. It is to the sea that man must turn with his inquisitiveness, his ability to reason, his strength and perserverance, his ships, and his instruments to explore and study these buried landscapes. From these studies man can hope to learn many secrets of how the features of his earth were formed and perhaps utilize this knowledge for the betterment of his own lot and that of his fellow man.

IV

T HE EARTH AS WE KNOW IT today is totally dependent upon its atmosphere. This blanket of air sustains all life on our planet. It is also a major geologic agent that helps to shape the land and make the soils. It sets in motion and continues a cycle of interrelationships between animate and inanimate things.

While we usually take the air around us for granted, it is an amazing storehouse of mysterious and curious wonders. Its function and influence are vital to man.

The earth's atmosphere was not always as it is today. Just as the earth formed its own waters, so it has produced its own atmosphere. The origin and subsequent development of the earth, its waters and its air are inextricably linked. According to the theory, in the early stages of development the earth's molten materials gave forth a hot, stinking, poisonous atmosphere that could not have supported life. But during a later stage the earth spewed forth a combination of gases and produced chemical compounds which were the foundations of life. The resulting plant life was able to convert the carbon dioxide of the atmosphere into oxygen, making possible the development of animal life and the atmosphere which surrounds our earth today.

In the following selection, George Gamow considers some of the important functions of the terrestrial atmosphere.

"Father Air"

WE LIVE on the bottom of a vast ocean of air which surrounds our globe as a thin transparent veil. One-quarter of the atmosphere is below the level of Santa Fe, New Mexico, which has an elevation of 7000 feet, one-half below the altitude of 16,500 feet, which is just the height of Mount Ararat, and three-quarters of it is below 30,000 feet, which is the height of Mount Everest. But highly rarefied fringes of terrestrial atmosphere extend hundreds of miles above the Earth's surface, and it is difficult to say where our atmosphere becomes merely the very thin gas which fills all interplanetary space. The total weight of terrestrial atmosphere is 5,000,000,000,000,000 tons, which, although a large number in itself, is nevertheless only one-third of one per cent of the total weight of water in the oceans. Atmospheric air is composed of 75.5 per cent nitrogen, 23.1 per cent oxygen, 0.9 per cent the inert gas argon, 0.03 per cent carbon dioxide, and negligible amounts of some

other gases. Up to the height of about 6 miles, air contains varying amounts of water vapor which originates from evaporation of moisture from the ocean and land surfaces and is carried upward by ascending convective currents. When the warm air rises it expands and becomes cooler, which accounts for the steady decrease in temperature with increasing height. At the altitude of 1½ miles, air temperature drops to the freezing point of water, and it continues to decrease steadily, dropping to about −100° F. at the altitude of 6 miles. The vertical convective currents do not penetrate beyond that height, and at greater altitudes air remains free of humidity and at a constant temperature. The part of the terrestrial atmosphere extending up to the height of 6 miles is known as the *troposphere*, and the physical phenomena occurring in it are of paramount importance for life on the Earth's surface. Storms, hurricanes, tornadoes, and typhoons originate here; all kinds of clouds are formed, to shower rain, snow, and hail on our heads. Beyond the upper limits of the troposphere conditions are much quieter and the sky is always blue. This is the *stratosphere,* through which pilots of airliners like to fly. The change of temperature with increasing altitude in the atmosphere is shown in the illustration.

With the exception of the chemically inert gas argon, all components of air play an important role in supporting life on the Earth. Proteins, which form the major part of all living organisms, are composed essentially of carbon, hydrogen, oxygen, and nitrogen. Growing plants get their carbon by absorbing and decomposing atmospheric carbon dioxide under the action of sunlight. Carbon is used to build sugars and other organic material, while oxygen is liberated back into the atmosphere. Hydrogen and oxygen in the form of water are brought in through the roots from the soil, where water gathers from rainfall. Atmospheric nitrogen is assimilated by certain bacteria in the soil, and turned into a variety of fertilizing material necessary for the growth of plants. Thus it is only fair that, when we speak about "Mother Earth," we do not forget "Father Air."

Plants and animals living on the surface of the earth exert, on their side, a considerable influence on the composition of the atmosphere. It has been estimated that plants consume yearly 500 billion tons of carbon dioxide, transforming it into organic materials. This figure is about one-third of the total carbon-dioxide content of the atmosphere, and if the supply were not constantly replenished it would run out in three short years. It may be mentioned here that only one-tenth of the total carbon-dioxide consumption is due to grass, bushes, and trees, the other nine-tenths being accounted for by algae in the oceans. The consumption of atmospheric carbon dioxide is compensated for by its formation in the processes of animal and plant respiration (plants consume oxygen at night), by the rotting of dead plants and fallen leaves, and by occasional forest fires; therefore it maintains a steady balance through the millennia.

If there were no organic life on the Earth, atmospheric oxygen would gradually disappear as a result of various inorganic oxidation processes, being transformed mostly into carbon dioxide. Such a situation seems to exist on Venus, whose atmosphere, according to spectroscopic studies, contains very large amounts of carbon dioxide and no detectable trace of free oxygen. This fact represents a strong indication that there is no life on the surface of that planet.

Another important function of terrestrial atmosphere is that it turns the Earth into a giant greenhouse, keeping it at a mean temperature of about 60°F., higher than it would be otherwise. The functioning of greenhouses, in which such plants as orchids and strawberries are grown, is based on the fact that glass, being almost completely transparent to visible light, which brings most of the Sun's energy, is opaque to the heat rays which are emitted by the object warmed up by the Sun's radiation. Thus, solar energy entering through the glass roof of a greenhouse is trapped inside and maintains a temperature well above the outside temperature. In the case of our atmosphere the role of glass is played by carbon dioxide and water vapor, which, even though present in minor amounts, absorb very strongly heat rays emitted from the Earth's warm surface and radiate them back to the Earth. Thus the excess heat which is removed from the Earth's surface during the daytime by the convective air currents is resupplied during the cold nights. The moderating effect of the atmosphere can best be demonstrated by comparing the Earth with the Moon, which

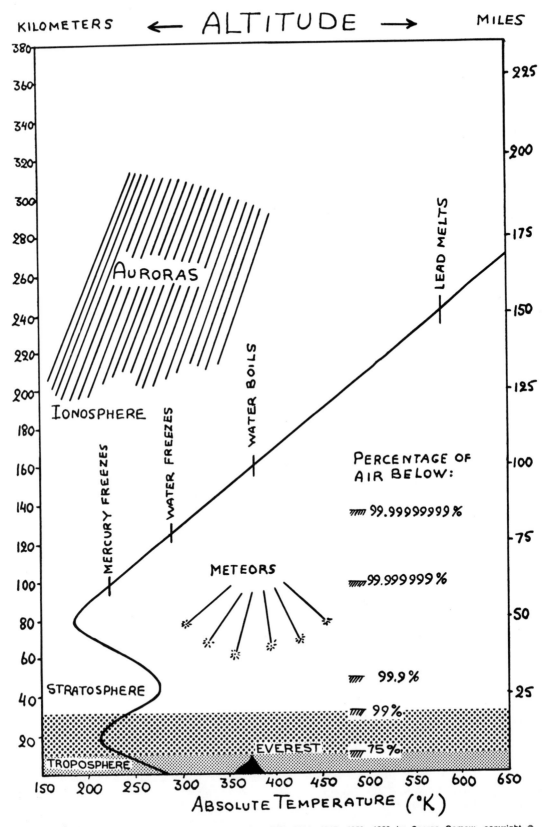

KILOMETERS ← ALTITUDE → MILES

AURORAS

IONOSPHERE

MERCURY FREEZES

WATER FREEZES

WATER BOILS

LEAD MELTS

PERCENTAGE OF
AIR BELOW:

99.99999999%

99.999999%

METEORS

99.9%

99%

STRATOSPHERE

EVEREST   75%

TROPOSPHERE

ABSOLUTE TEMPERATURE (°K)

Cross-section of the terrestrial atmosphere.

gets exactly the same amount of heat but has no atmosphere. Measurements of the Moon's surface temperature, carried out by special heat-sensitive instruments known as *bolometers,* show that on the illuminated side of the Moon the temperature of the rocks rises to 214°F., while it drops to −243°F. on the Moon's dark side. Thus if our Earth had no atmosphere water would boil during the daytime, and alcohol would freeze during the night!

While controlling the visible sunlight to keep the Earth's surface warm and comfortable, our atmosphere protects us from various much less pleasant kinds of radiation from the Sun. Apart from visible light, our Sun is known to emit rather large quantities of ultraviolet radiation, X rays, and high-energy particles, which would have a deadly effect on plant and animal life if permitted to penetrate all the way to the surface. But all these dangerous rays are absorbed in the upper layers of the atmosphere, and only a negligible fraction of ultraviolet comes through in just the proper amount to tan the bodies of vacationers on the beaches.

Last but not least, is the mechanical protection our atmosphere gives us against constant bombardment by meteorites of various sizes (with the exception of the biggest ones, which come rarely), and against artificial satellites and the rockets used to put them into orbit, which completely burn and disintegrate after their re-entry into the air.

V

F

OR ABOUT TWO THOUSAND MILLION years the earth's atmosphere has
retained its delicate balance of components. It is today mainly a mixture of two invisible gases, nitrogen and oxygen, in a ratio of about
four to one, a little carbon dioxide, traces of inert gases and varying
amounts of such impurities as dust, smoke, spores and water vapor.
The oxygen of the atmosphere sustains life. The nitrogen seems to
serve primarily to dilute the oxygen, as soda water dilutes the syrup
of a carbonated drink. The impurities have a direct effect on man with
respect to visibility, sunshine, precipitation, diffusion of light and other
natural phenomena.

The authors of the next selection, Samuel Namowitz and Donald
Stone, have summarized some of the significant information geologists
have gathered about the nature of our planet's atmosphere.

The Nature of the Atmosphere

From *Earth Science: The World We Live In* by Samuel N. Namowitz and Donald B. Stone. Copyright ©1960 by Litton Educational Publishing, Inc.

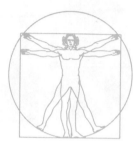

Recipe for Air

Put together a mixture of odorless, invisible gases consisting, by volume, of 78 per cent nitrogen, 21 per cent oxygen, and the remaining 1 per cent chiefly argon (0.94 per cent), a little carbon dioxide (0.03 per cent) and mere traces of neon, krypton, xenon, helium, and hydrogen. Add another trace of ozone, which has an odor. Such a mixture, practically odorless and as invisible as all of its parts, is the material we call *air*. And this air, covering the entire surface of the earth and reaching a height of at least 600 miles as it thins out into empty space, forms a great shell of mixed gases to which the name *atmosphere* is given. The atmosphere, then, is the entire gaseous shell, while the air is the material of which this shell is made.

The air that we have put together is dry and without dust. Air in this condition is referred to as "pure dry air." But in nature such air never exists, for air always contains some water vapor and some dust. Before discussing this further, let us see how we acquire our knowledge of the atmosphere.

Exploring the Atmosphere

If the atmosphere were only four or five miles high, all our studies of it might be made by direct observation. But since it extends upward more than 600 miles, it is obvious that some of our knowledge about it must come indirectly. Here is a brief listing of both direct and indirect sources of information.

Direct observations have been made by man himself: (1) on mountains to heights of about 5½ miles; (2) in balloons to a record height of almost 20 miles; (3) in jet planes to a record height of about 24 miles. Instrument-carrying balloons have ascended to heights of about 28 miles; instrument-carrying satellites have circled the earth at heights varying from 130 miles to about 2500 miles, thus extending the range of instrument observations far beyond the top of the atmosphere.

Information about the atmosphere can be obtained *indirectly* in several ways: (1) By using the spectroscope to analyze the light of the *aurora borealis*, or northern lights, scientists may determine what gases

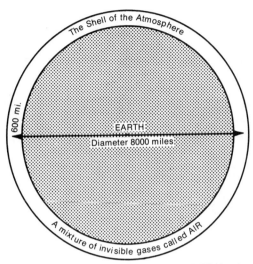

The earth and its atmosphere are drawn to scale in this diagram.

are in the parts of the atmosphere where the lights appear. At the same time the height of that portion of the atmosphere may be measured. (2) Study of meteors, or "shooting stars," may give information about upper air temperatures. (3) Study of the reflection or absorption of sound waves, radio waves, television waves, and radar waves may give information about the existence of "layers" in the atmosphere that differ markedly from the rest of it in such characteristics as temperature and electrical properties.

How Much Atmosphere?

Man has risen 24 miles into the atmosphere and has floated balloons to a height of 28 miles. While most clouds occur under the 7-mile altitude, the extremely rare noctilucent (night-luminous) clouds show the presence of air at about 50 miles. The fiery rock fragments we call meteors flare up because of friction with air at even greater heights. But the 600-mile figure given as the approximate limit of the atmosphere is derived from measurements of northern

lights, for these are known to be caused by electrical discharges in very thin *air*, just as the glow of a neon tube is caused by the passage of electricity through the thin gas it contains.

The Air and Its Parts

Like the gases of which it is composed, air is highly compressible and highly elastic. Because air is compressible, it can be squeezed together so that it becomes denser. Because air is elastic, it expands when pressure on it is reduced. Air is very light in comparison with solids and liquids; it weighs only 1.2 ounces per cubic foot at sea level and is only 1/800 as heavy as water. But the quantity of air in the atmosphere is very great and its total weight amounts to almost 15 pounds for every square inch of the earth's surface. Air supports life on the earth, and it is the material in which weather is produced and flight is maintained.

Oxygen is the part of the air that living things require for the conversion of food into energy. *Nitrogen* forms the bulk of the air, diluting the oxygen much as water dilutes orange juice in an orangeade. *Carbon dioxide*, used by green plants in making starch, is also important in retaining heat near the earth's surface. *Ozone* is a highly active form of oxygen, and a remarkable absorber of ultraviolet light from the sun. It has a sharp odor like that of a freshly struck match. It is the only gas in the air that has an odor. Ozone may occasionally be smelled in the air near sparking electrical devices, since the electrical sparks turn oxygen into ozone.

Argon, neon, xenon and *krypton* are gases of no known importance in the atmosphere, though neon is familiar to us as the gas of neon signs, and argon is used in ordinary electric-light bulbs.

Hydrogen and *helium* are the lightest of all gases and are therefore used in lifting balloons, but the amounts of hydrogen and

Atmospheric phenomena and explorations.

Courtesy of Litton Educational Publishing, Inc.

helium in the atmosphere are tiny, except possibly at very great heights.

Water vapor is water that has evaporated into the air and is present as a gas. Water vapor is as "dry," as invisible, and as odorless as any other gas in the air. Weather scientists regard it as the most important gas in the air, for when it condenses it forms the clouds and the rains that are necessary for all life. Compared with other gases, it is a good absorber of the sun's energy.

Dust, of course, is not a gas, but it is an important "weather" part of the air, for tiny dust particles act as "condensation nuclei" around which water vapor may condense to form cloud and rain droplets. The principal kinds of dust are: (1) dust blown up from dry soil; (2) dust from volcanic eruptions; (3) plant pollen and bacteria; (4) soot from smoking fires; (5) salt particles from sea spray. Soot and salt are especially effective in helping water vapor to condense. Microscopic dust particles are also the cause of atmospheric haze.

How the Air Compresses Itself

A mountain climber finds breathing increasingly difficult the higher he climbs. Obviously it is because the air is thinner at greater heights, and each lungful of air contains fewer of the oxygen molecules he requires. In fact, at 18,000 feet, there is only half as much oxygen in a lungful of air as there is at sea level. Why should this be?

As mentioned before, air is highly compressible, and the upper air so compresses the air below it, that half the total weight of the air lies within about 3½ miles (18,000 feet) of the earth's surface, and almost 99 per cent of its total weight lies under the 20-mile level. The atmosphere can be compared to a stack of fluffy pies, one on top of the other. Though all are of the same material, the bottom one would be badly crushed, while the top one would be as fluffy as when removed from the oven.

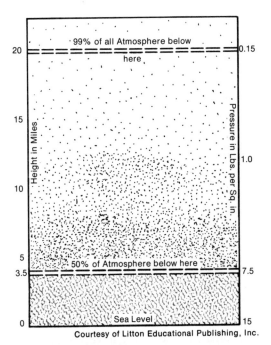

Through its own weight, the atmosphere compresses itself to such an extent that half of all the atmosphere lies below the 3.5 mile level.

Is Air Always the Same?

The air in the atmosphere is mixed so perfectly that *pure dry air* has almost exactly the same composition all over the world up to a height of at least 20 miles. The percentage of carbon dioxide is slightly higher near volcanoes and where large quantities of fuel are burned. The percentage of ozone, almost too small to mention, reaches a maximum of 1 part in 100,000 parts of air at about 20 miles elevation. Even small changes in the percentage of this "ozone layer" seem to be closely connected with weather changes near the earth's surface. Except for these two cases, there is no appreciable variation in the percentages of the components of pure dry air.

The percentage of water vapor in the air varies widely, from almost none to as high as 4 per cent by volume, depending on location, elevation, season, and time of day. Of course, when the percentage of water vapor is included in an analysis of the air, the percentages of the other components are no longer the constant figures given [at the beginning] of this chapter. For example, when air contains 2.6 per cent water vapor, it has 76.05 per cent nitrogen, 20.4 per cent oxygen, 0.9 per cent argon, and 0.05 per cent all other gases.

The dust content of the air is greatest in desert areas, near volcanoes during eruption, near factories, and in ocean areas where sea spray evaporates and leaves invisible salt particles in the air.

The Four Layers of the Atmosphere

Scientists studying the atmospheric *phenomena* (things visible or observable) have decided that the atmosphere consists of four distinct layers, very different from each other. These layers have been named *troposphere, stratosphere, ionosphere,* and *exosphere.*

The *troposphere* extends from the earth's surface to a height that varies from about 5 miles at the Poles to about 11 miles at the Equator. In middle latitudes it is about 7 miles high. It is the region of clouds and changing weather conditions, and derives its name from the Greek word *tropikos,* meaning "turn," because the air in it is continually turning over in great currents and storms. Its other outstanding characteristic is a steady drop in temperature with increasing altitude at the average rate of about 3½ degrees Fahrenheit per 1000 feet (in still air). The point at which the temperature ceases to fall is called the *tropopause.* As its name suggests, the tropopause marks the top of the troposphere. The warmer the climate at sea level, generally, the higher the tropopause.

The *stratosphere* extends from the tropopause to a height of about 50 miles. Its name tells us that it is the region of layer-like, or horizontal, air movement. Winds are strong and steady, skies are always clear, and there is almost no dust or water vapor. Flying conditions in the lower stratosphere are almost ideal, but the occupants of an airship must be protected against the extreme cold, the low pressure, and the lack of oxygen. At the bottom of the stratosphere the temperature is very low, about −67° F in latitude 45°. In the stratosphere, according to recent observations, the temperature rises in most places until the 150,-000-foot level (about 28 miles) is reached. At this level the temperature is 90° F or higher. Then it drops again to well below freezing at about 50 miles. Here the *stratopause* marks the top of the stratosphere.

The *ionosphere* extends from the stratopause to a height of 300 miles or more. Here the temperature rises steadily right to the very top of the atmosphere, where it is believed to reach 4000° F. The very thin air of the ionosphere contains large numbers of electrically charged air particles called *ions.* These ions are the cause of many strange electrical effects. At some levels of the ionosphere they help to make the glow we know as the *aurora.* At other levels they collect in layers which reflect ordinary radio waves back to the earth. The best-known of these layers is called the Kennelly-Heaviside Layer. By reflecting ordinary radio waves back to the earth over and over again, these layers help the waves to pass around the earth. Short radio waves, television waves, and radar waves are not stopped by the Kennelly-Heaviside Layer and thus may escape into space.

The *exosphere* is the outermost layer of the atmosphere, beyond the ionosphere.

Observations made by satellites and lunar rockets during the International Geophysical Year showed that two bands of intense and deadly cosmic radiation surround the earth high above the exosphere. The first band occurs between altitudes of 1400 and 3000 miles above the earth's surface, and is most intense at about

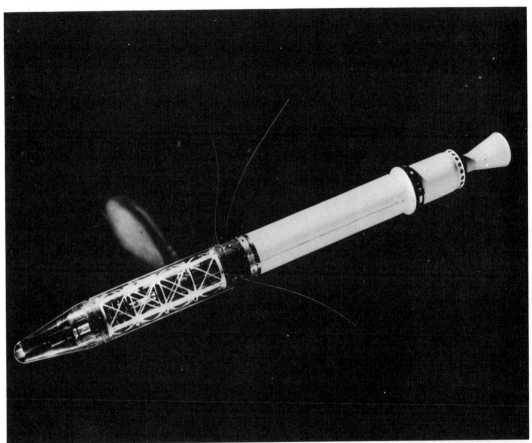

A model of Explorer I, the first United States earth satellite and the discoverer of previously-unknown radiation bands high above the exosphere. Explorer I was launched January 1, 1958, during the IGY.

2000 miles. The second and larger band begins at about 8000 miles above the surface and continues to a height of about 12,000 miles from the surface. Since man will have to penetrate these bands of radiation if he is to travel in space, it is most important that we obtain information about them.

VI

A N INCONSPICUOUS MEMBER of the atmospheric mixture, water vapor never amounts to more than four per cent by volume of the air. However, it is important not only to life on earth, but to the functions of the atmosphere itself. This is so because it has special properties allowing it to function as an interceptor of radiation. Clouds, rainbows and sky colors are all created by the interplay of atmospheric moisture and sunlight.

Precipitation is one of the more important consequences of the presence of water vapor in the atmosphere. The authors of the following selection provide some important considerations about moisture origin, condensation, cloud formation, precipitation and other related topics.

Atmospheric Moisture and Precipitation

Humidity

IMPORTANCE OF WATER VAPOR

Water in gas form, or water vapor, in the atmosphere is referred to as *humidity*. Although it comprises only about 2 per cent of the total atmosphere, in terms of weather and climate water vapor is by all odds the single most important element of the air. Unlike most of the other gases, the proportion of humidity in the lower atmosphere varies considerably in both time and space (from nearly zero up to a maximum of 4 or 5 per cent) and this variability is of great importance for several reasons: (*a*) The amount of water vapor in a given mass of air is an index of the atmosphere's potential for yielding precipitation, one of the two major climatic elements. (*b*) Through its absorptive effects on earth radiation it regulates the rate of heat loss from the earth and thereby affects surface temperatures. (*c*) The greater the amount of humidity, the greater the amount of latent or potential energy stored up in the atmosphere for the development and growth of atmospheric disturbances or storms. The amount and vertical distribution of water vapor frequently determine whether an air mass will be stable and resist upward movement, or unstable and buoyant. (*d*) The humidity is likewise an important factor affecting the human body's rate of cooling, *i.e.*, the *sensible temperature*.

EVAPORATION AND THE SOURCES OF HUMIDITY

Like all other atmospheric gases, water vapor is invisible. It is derived from water in the liquid and solid form through the process of *evaporation*. The amount and rapidity of evaporation from a water surface depend upon the temperature of the air, its aridity, and its movement. On very hot, dry, and windy days evaporation is rapid. Certain generalizations regarding the distribution of actual evaporation are climatically significant: (*a*) Evaporation over oceans is greater than over continents where the water supply is more meager. (*b*) Evaporation is at a maximum in the low latitudes and it decreases poleward. Actually evaporation is greater at latitudes

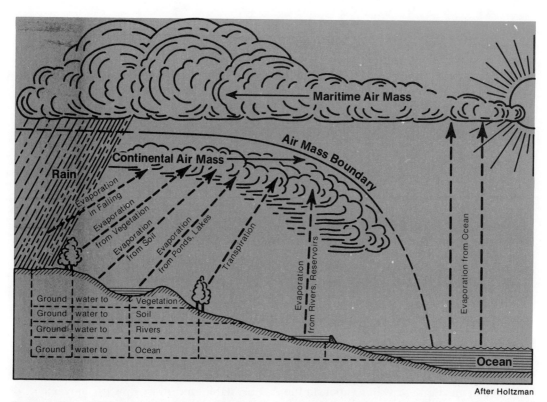

After Holtzman

Figure 1 *The hydrologic cycle. As dry continental air masses evaporate land moisture and carry it to the sea, so maritime air masses transfer moisture evaporated from the oceans to the continents where it falls as rain.*

10 to 20°, where the air is drier and the winds stronger and steadier, than at the equator.

The primary source of atmospheric humidity is the great oceans which cover approximately three-quarters of the earth's surface. By winds and diffusion methods, the water vapor evaporated from these bodies of water through the expenditure of solar energy is carried in over the continents. Less important, but nevertheless significant, sources of atmospheric moisture are the moist land surfaces, the vegetation cover, and the minor bodies of water. Plants give off more moisture to the air than does bare ground but not so much as does a freely exposed water surface. A constant turnover is forever in progress as regards the atmosphere's water vapor, additions be-

ing made through evaporation of water in its solid and liquid states, while some is being lost to the atmosphere by *condensation* and *precipitation*. By the process of condensation, water vapor, a gas, is changed back into the liquid or solid state, while through evaporation the liquid or solid water is converted into invisible gaseous water vapor. Half the water vapor in the air lies below an altitude of 6,500 ft.

THE HYDROLOGIC CYCLE

For some time it has been known that the precipitation which falls upon the continents is far in excess of the runoff from the lands in the form of rivers and glaciers. Probably not more than 30 per cent of continental precipitation finds its way back to the oceans as water and ice. Much of the remaining 70 per cent of the continental precipitation is evaporated from the lands and carried back to the oceans by the seaward-and-equatorward-moving dry polar continental air masses (figure 1). In the cycle of atmospheric exchange between land and sea, moist tropical maritime air masses carry oceanic moisture poleward into the middle-latitude continents, where it is cooled and precipitated. Conversely dry polar continental air masses carry much of the evaporated land moisture back again to the tropical oceans. The great surges of polar air moving southward over the United States are vast invisible "rivers," evaporating from the lands and transporting this moisture in vapor form back to the Gulf of Mexico and the tropical Atlantic.

LATENT ENERGY IN WATER VAPOR

It is common knowledge that energy is required in the form of heat to change ice (solid) into water (liquid) and water into vapor or steam (gas). The unit of heat energy, the calorie, is the amount of heat required to raise the temperature of a gram of water one degree centigrade. But it takes 79 calories to convert a gram of ice into a gram of water at freezing temperature, and 607 calories to evaporate the gram of water at 32° and convert it into water vapor at the same temperature. Since energy is required to change the solid into a liquid, and likewise the liquid into a gas, it follows that water vapor contains more potential energy than liquid water and water, in turn, more than ice. This stored-up energy in water vapor is known as *latent heat,* or *latent energy.* For the most part it is transformed sun energy, which has been employed in evaporating water, ice, or snow and converting them into water vapor. One reason why bodies of water heat slowly is that so much energy is consumed in evaporating at their surfaces. That evaporation requires heat is evident from the cool sen-

sation experienced when the skin is moistened with water or, even better, with alcohol. In this case heat is subtracted from the skin to convert the liquid into a gas. If energy is consumed in the process of evaporation, then, conversely, energy should again be released during condensation. This released heat, known as the *latent heat of condensation,* is an important source of energy in the growth of storms and in the production of precipitation. On a night when condensation takes place, cooling is retarded by the liberation of so much latent heat.

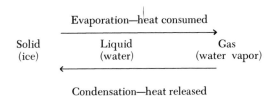

ATMOSPHERIC HUMIDITY

The capacity of the air for containing water vapor depends almost exclusively on its temperature. Air that is warm or hot is able to contain much more water vapor than air that is cold. Moreover, the capacity of air for water vapor *increases at an increasing rate* as the temperature rises. This is indicated by the following table and by figure 2. Thus by increasing the temperature of a cubic foot of air 10°, from 30

TABLE 1. Maximum Water-vapor Capacity of 1 Cu. Ft. of Air at Varying Temperatures

Temperature, Degrees Fahrenheit	Water Vapor, Grains	Difference between Successive 10° Intervals
30	1.9	
40	2.9	1.0
50	4.1	1.2
60	5.7	1.6
70	8.0	2.3
80	10.9	2.9
90	14.7	3.8
100	19.7	5.0

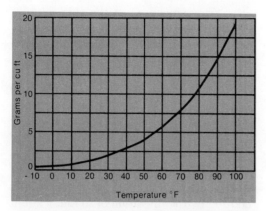

Figure 2 *Not only does the capacity of air to contain water vapor increase as the temperature of the air rises, but it increases at an increasing rate.*

to 40°, the moisture capacity is advanced only 1 grain, while a similar 10° increase, from 90 to 100°, results in an increase of 5 grains. It is evident that the air on a hot summer day is able to contain much more moisture than is cold winter air and is likely, therefore, to have greater potentialities for abundant precipitation. Air over Madison, Wis., in July has a water-vapor capacity seven to eight times what it is in January. When a given mass of air contains all the water vapor that it is capable of retaining, it is said to be *saturated*.

Distribution of Humidity. The moisture content of the atmosphere is described in several ways. The actual amount of water vapor in the air is expressed either as specific humidity or as absolute humidity and for the purpose of this book they may be considered as similar. They both express actual water-vapor content of the air and hence are of some significance in gauging the atmosphere's capacity for precipitation. *Specific humidity* is the weight of water vapor in a unit weight of air and is usually expressed as the number of grams of water vapor contained in one kilogram of air. *Absolute humidity* refers to weight of water vapor per unit volume of air.

Since the earth's surface is the source of

atmospheric humidity, it is to be expected that the *vertical distribution* of specific and absolute humidity shows the highest concentration near the earth's surface and a rapid decrease with altitude. The average *zonal* (north-south) *distribution* of specific humidity is largely a function of temperature and hence it is highest in the low latitudes near the equator and decreases poleward (figure 3). It is not unexpected also that the *seasonal distribution* of specific and absolute humidity shows much higher values in summer than in winter. Over north central United States in July air contains three to six times as much humidity as does the January air.

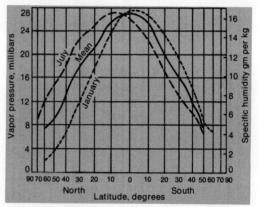

Figure 3 *Zonal distribution of the water-vapor content of the air. Specific humidity is highest in the vicinity of the equator and decreases toward the poles. There is a northward displacement in July and a southward displacement in January because of a similar distribution of temperature. Specific humidity at each latitude is higher in summer than in winter.*

Relative Humidity. Relative humidity is always expressed in the form of a ratio, fraction, or percentage. It represents the amount of water vapor actually present in the air (absolute humidity) compared with the greatest amount that could be present at the same temperature. When the relative humidity reaches 100 per cent, the air is said to be saturated. As an illustration: air at 70° can contain approximately 8 grains of water vapor per cubic foot. If it actually contains only 6 grains (its absolute humidity), then it is only three-fourths saturated, and its relative humidity is 75 per cent. Relative humidity can be altered either by changing the amount of water vapor or by varying the capacity of the air, *i.e.*, changing its temperature. The following table shows how air which was saturated at 40° acquires successively lower relative humidities simply by increasing its temperature,

Temperature, Degrees Fahrenheit	Absolute Humidity, Grains	Relative Humidity, Per Cent Saturated
40	2.9	100
50	2.9	71
60	2.9	51
70	2.9	36
80	2.9	27
90	2.9	19

the water-vapor content remaining unchanged. Relative humidity is an important determinant of the amount and rate of evaporation; hence it is a critical climatic factor in the rate of moisture and temperature loss by plants and animals, including human beings.

Various humidity relationships are illustrated by figures 4 and 5. Figure 4 shows a cubic foot of air subject to three different temperatures. At 0°F. only ½ grain of invisible water vapor can exist in a cubic foot. If the temperature rises to 40°F., nearly 3 grains of water vapor can exist in that same cubic foot of air, and at 80°F. there can be nearly 11 grains of water vapor in the same space. In all these cases, saturation conditions, or 100 per cent relative humidities, are assumed. If any of the cubes in figure 4 are cooled appreciably, the invisible water vapor will be condensed out as visible water or ice particles.

In figure 5 the same cubic-foot samples are shown except that they now represent unsaturated conditions; *i.e.*, they do not contain all the water vapor possible at those temperatures. The cube on the extreme left has only ¼ grain of water vapor. Since this is only one-half of what can be present under saturated conditions (see cube at left in figure 4), the relative humidity is therefore ¼ grain divided by ½ grain, or 50 per cent. The middle cube in figure 5 contains only ½ grain of water vapor as compared with nearly 3 grains at saturation, making a relative humidity in this case of about 17 per cent. The same reasoning gives a relative humidity of about 91 per cent for the cube on the extreme right. A comparison of the cube on the extreme left in figure 4 with the center cube in figure 5, *both of which contain identical amounts of water vapor*, reveals the former with 100 per cent relative humidity and the latter with only 17 per cent. This explains why relative humidity ordinarily goes down as temperature rises on a hot summer day and rises as temperature falls on a cool night.

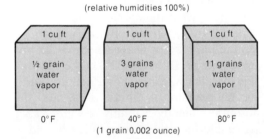

Figure 4 *Saturated conditions.*

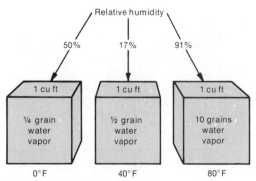

Figure 5 *Unsaturated conditions.*

The zonal distribution of relative humidity shows a strong maximum in the vicinity of the equator from which point there is a decline poleward with minima located at about 25 to 35°N. and S. (figure 6). These are the regions of the subtropical anticyclones. Poleward from the subtropics as temperature declines the relative humidity increases and maxima are located in the higher middle latitudes (60° ±N. and S.). For the *daily period* relative humidity is usually highest in the early morning and lowest in midafternoon.

Dew Point and Condensation. If air that is not saturated is sufficiently cooled, its capacity for moisture thereby being reduced, a temperature is eventually reached at which the mass of air is saturated, even though the amount of water vapor has not been altered. This critical temperature at which saturation is reached is called the *dew point.* If air is cooled below the dew point, then the excess of water vapor, over and above what the air can contain at that temperature, is given off in the form of minute particles of water (if above 32°) or sometimes ice (if below 32°) and *condensation* has taken place. For example, when the temperature of the air is 80° and the absolute humidity 8 grains of water vapor per cubic foot, then the relative humidity is 73 per cent (table 1). If this mass of air is gradually reduced in temperature so that its capacity for water vapor is lowered, it eventually reaches the dew point 70° and is therefore saturated at that temperature. Further cooling below the saturation point leads to condensation, the amount of water vapor condensed being the difference between the capacity of air at the different temperatures. Thus a cubic foot of saturated air at 70°, if reduced to 60°, will result in 2.3 grains of water vapor being condensed, this being the difference between the capacities of a cubic foot of air at those two temperatures. An equivalent amount of cooling of saturated air at different temperatures does not, however, yield the same amount of condensed water vapor. If a cubic foot of saturated air at 90° has its temperature reduced 20° (to 70°), 6.7 grains of water vapor are condensed (table 1), but a further cooling of 20° (to 50°) releases only 3.9 grains, and the next 20° drop only 2.2 grains. It is obvious that warm summer air has greater potentialities for abundant precipitation than does cold winter air.

Condensation

Condensation occurs in the atmosphere when a state of saturation is reached, or in other words, when the relative humidity

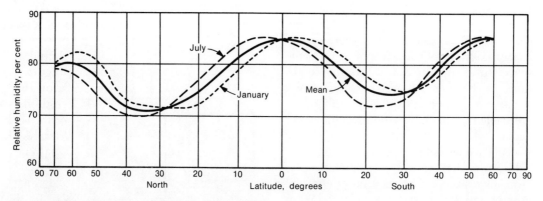

Figure 6 *Zonal distribution of relative humidity. Note that the north-south distribution of relative humidity is quite different from that of specific humidity (Figure 3).*

approaches 100 per cent. The condition of saturation may be brought about either by reducing the temperature of the air below the dew point or by increasing the humidity in the air to the saturation point. The first of these two processes is much the more important in causing large-scale condensation, including the formation of all precipitation. By cooling the atmosphere its capacity for water vapor is lowered, and if sufficiently reduced, condensation must result. The dew point of any mass of air is closely related to its relative humidity. When the relative humidity is high, and the air is close to saturation point, only a slight amount of cooling may be required before the dew point is reached and condensation begins. On the other hand, when relative humidity is low, as it usually is over the hot deserts, a large amount of cooling is required before the dew point is reached.

Condensation, therefore, depends upon two variables: (a) the amount of cooling and (b) the relative humidity of the air. If the dew point is not reached until the temperature falls below 32°, some of the condensed water vapor *may* be in the form of tiny ice crystals (white frost, snow, and some clouds); if condensation occurs above the freezing point, it must be in the liquid state (dew, fog, and most clouds). Actually, much condensation which occurs at temperatures below freezing is in the liquid rather than the solid form and it appears to persist in this liquid form down to temperatures of $-40°$F.

All condensation in the free atmosphere occurs around hygroscopic nuclei. The most universal condensation nuclei are those of the sea-salt variety. These small salt particles are widely distributed throughout the lower atmosphere by wind. A more active type of hygroscopic nucleus, but more limited in its distribution, is that which is put into the air through the burn-

ing of sulphurous fuels such as coal and oil. The very dense fogs in the smoky atmosphere over low-lying industrial areas are associated with this second type of nuclei.

CONDENSATION FORMS AT OR NEAR EARTH'S SURFACE

By direct cooling processes such as conduction and radiation from the overlying air to the cold earth, and by the mixing of two air masses of unlike temperatures and humidities, relatively shallow layers of air may be cooled below the dew point. However, the condensation forms (*dew, white frost,* and *fog*) resulting from the above-mentioned processes are of relatively small scale and are usually confined to the earth's surface or to shallow layers of surface air. Appreciable rainfall probably never results from such cooling processes. The cooling of deep and extensive masses of air well below the dew point, with associated large-scale condensation in the form of thick cloud masses capable of producing abundant precipitation, is always the result of expansion in rising air masses.

Fog. Of those forms of condensation which occur at the earth's surface, fog is decidedly of the greatest importance climatically speaking.

A very common type of land fog, known as *radiation* or *ground-inversion* fog, results from the cooling by radiation and conduction processes of shallow layers of quiet air overlying a chilled land surface (figure 7). Clear nights with little wind favor their development. They are deeper and more prevalent in valleys and depressions where, as a result of air drainage, the colder, heavier air collects. Radiation fogs usually are short-lived, being characteristic of the cooler night hours, for they tend to dissipate with sun heating during the day. In the vicinity of large industrial cities where sulphurous condensation nuclei are numerous they are likely to be denser and more persistent.

Another very common type of fog is known as the *advection-radiation* type which develops in mild, humid air as it moves over a colder surface and is chilled by radiation and conduction (figure 7). Here the emphasis is on *moving*, rather than quiet, air. Fogs of this origin are very common over oceans, especially in summer, along seacoasts and the shores of large inland lakes, and over middle-latitude land surfaces in winter. They are particularly prevalent in the vicinity of cool ocean currents. Advection fogs in the interiors of continents are commonly associated with a poleward flow of mild, humid air from lower latitudes over a cold and snow-covered surface (figure 7). In general, advection fogs are less local in development than is the simple radiation type, and they tend to persist for longer periods of time so that days as well as nights may remain shrouded.

Still another fog type is that which is associated with belts of frontal rainfall. It

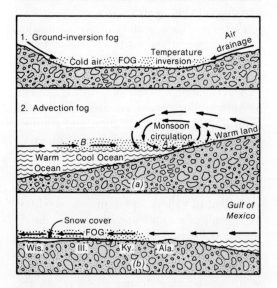

Figure 7 *Common types of fog and methods of their formation.*

originates as a consequence of falling rain saturating the cool surface air.

Distribution of Fog. Generalizations concerning fog distribution are not easy to make. Without much doubt it is more common over oceans than over continents and it is likewise more frequent over oceans in middle and higher latitudes than over those in the tropics. On the continents it is the coastal areas that have the greatest number of days with fog (figure 8).

Within the United States fog days are most frequent along the Pacific Coast, the North Atlantic Seaboard, and over the Appalachian Highlands. The least foggy area is the dry interior western country.

CONDENSATION FORMS IN THE
FREE ATMOSPHERE

Although condensation forms in the surface air (dew, white frost, fog) are of some importance, they are, nevertheless, insignificant climatically compared with precipitation which is a product of condensation in the form of clouds. Clouds of great vertical thickness, capable of yielding moderate or abundant precipitation, are the product of one process of atmospheric cooling almost exclusively, *viz.*, cooling as a result of expansion in upward-moving thick air masses.

When air rises, no matter what the reason, it expands because there is less weight of air upon it at the higher altitudes. Thus if a mass of dry air at sea level rises to an altitude of about 18,000 ft., the pressure upon it is reduced one-half, and consequently its volume is doubled. A cubic foot of air at sea level would then, if carried to that altitude, occupy 2 cu. ft. In making room for itself as ascent and gradual expansion take place, other air has to be displaced. The work done in pushing aside the surrounding air requires energy, and this necessary energy is subtracted from the rising air mass in the form of heat, resulting in a low-

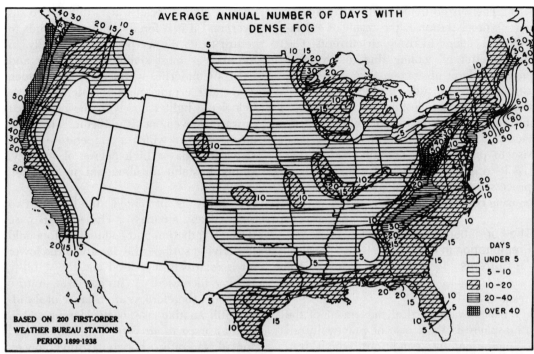

Courtesy of U. S. Weather Bureau

Figure 8 *Map showing areas where fog occurs most often.*

ering of its temperature. Conversely, when air descends from higher altitudes, it is compressed by the denser air at lower levels. Work is done upon it, and its temperature consequently is raised. It is a truism, therefore, that rising air cools, while descending air is warmed. The temperature changes occurring in the rising or subsiding air mass are not the result of additions of heat to, or withdrawals of heat from, outside sources, but rather are the consequence of internal processes of expansion and contraction. This is spoken of as *adiabatic temperature change.*

The rate of cooling or heating resulting from vertical movement of dry or nonsaturated air is constant and is approximately 5½° per 1,000 ft. change in altitude. This is the dry adiabatic rate. The rate of cooling of ascending air, therefore, is considerably more rapid than is the normal decrease of

temperature (about 3.3° per 1,000 ft.) with increasing elevation, or the lapse rate. These two rates, the adiabatic rate and the lapse rate, should be clearly distinguished as being very different things, for one represents the cooling of a rising and therefore moving mass of air, while the other represents the change in air temperature that would be recorded by a thermometer carried up through the atmosphere by a balloon or kite.

Heated air continues to rise until it reaches air layers of its own temperature and density. It bears repeating that *this process of cooling, by expansion of rising air currents, is the only one capable of reducing the temperature of thick and extensive masses of air below the dew point.* It is the only one, therefore, which is capable of producing condensation on such a large scale that abundant precipitation results. There is no doubt that nearly all the earth's precipitation is the result of expansion and cooling in rising air currents. The direct result of cooling due to ascent is *clouds*, a form of condensation characteristic of air at altitudes usually well above the earth's surface, just as dew, white frost, and fog are forms characteristic of the surface air. Not all clouds, to be sure, give rise to precipitation, but all precipitation has its origin in clouds and is the result of processes that are supplementary to those causing condensation.

The Formation of Clouds and Precipitation in Ascending Air Currents

STABILITY

Since upward vertical movement of the atmosphere is the cause of practically all precipitation, the conditions which promote or hinder such movements are of prime importance. When air resists vertical movement and tends to remain in the original position, it is said to be *stable*. Atmospheric stability may be likened to a cone resting upon its broad base. Such a

cone is stable because it is difficult to tip over, and if it is forcibly tipped, it tends to return to its former position. Normally an air mass is most stable when colder and drier air underlies warmer air. Under such a vertical arrangement the denser air is below the lighter air, with the result that upward movement is difficult. Therefore an air mass in which a temperature inversion exists has a high degree of stability. In highly stable air abundant precipitation is unlikely.

Stability is promoted in at least two ways. If any air mass is chilled at its base through radiation and conduction to a cold underlying surface, the density of the lower air is relatively increased and the stability is also increased. A surface temperature inversion, therefore, is an instance of stability. Still another way of developing stability in a mass of air is for it to subside and spread laterally (horizontal divergence). Such a process of stabilization occurs in high-pressure anticyclonic systems.

The relative stability of an air mass may be determined by noting its vertical temperature distribution or lapse rate and comparing it with the adiabatic rate. A small

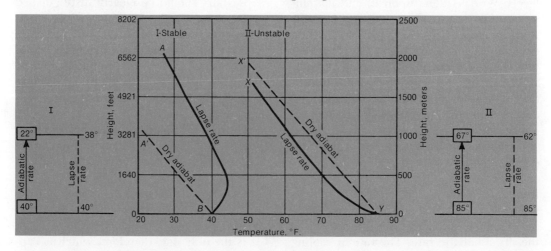

Figure 9 *Atmospheric stability and instability. When the lapse rate exceeds the adiabatic rate, instability prevails. When the reverse is true, the air is stable.*

or weak lapse rate (less than the adiabatic rate of 5½° per 1,000 ft.), and especially one in which the temperature increases with altitude, indicates stable air.

INSTABILITY

When air does not resist upward vertical displacement but, on the contrary, has a tendency to move upward away from its original position, a condition of *instability* prevails. Under such a condition where the air is buoyant, upward vertical movement is prevalent and cloud and precipitation are likely. Instability may be likened to a cone delicately balanced upon its small apex, for here the slightest impulse will cause it to tip over. Instability is characteristic of warm, humid air in which there is a rapid vertical decrease in temperature and humidity, *i.e.*, a steep lapse rate. When the lapse rate is greater than the adiabatic rate of 5½°F. per 1,000 ft., a condition of instability prevails (figures 9 and 10).

Instability may be developed in an air

mass if it is warmed and humidified in its lower layers. In summer when air from the Gulf of Mexico flows in over the warm land of the Cotton Belt states it is heated from below, made unstable, and much thunderstorm rainfall results. Instability is likewise promoted in a thick air mass by forcing it to rise. Hence the air in any converging system such as a low-pressure cyclonic system is likely to become unstable. Moreover, when humid air that is mildly stable is *forced* to rise over mountain barriers or over colder wedges of air, the resulting condensation may add so much heat to the ascending air that it becomes actually unstable and so continues to rise with accompanying heavy precipitation. Such humid air, which was originally stable but was made unstable as a result of condensation associated with forced ascent, is said to be *conditionally unstable*.

Cloud Types

Clouds reflect the physical processes occurring in the atmosphere and consequently they are useful indicators of weather conditions. . . . A modest acquaintance with cloud types is highly useful to the geographer in his understanding of the daily weather out of which the composite climatic picture is composed. Only brief mention is made here of the 10 principal cloud types recognized in the international classification of clouds (figure 11).

FAMILY A: HIGH CLOUDS
(MEAN LOWER LEVEL 20,000 FT.)

1. *Cirrus.* Because of their high altitudes, all clouds of the cirrus family are composed of ice crystals instead of water droplets. Cirrus are thin featherlike clouds of delicate and fibrous appearance, white in color, and generally without shading. They may be brilliantly colored at sunset. When in the form of detached tufts and of irregular arrangement, they are indicators of fair

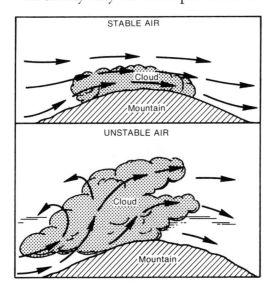

Figure 10 *Cloud formation in the forced ascent of stable and unstable air. With stable air, which is nonbuoyant, the clouds are not so thick and the resulting precipitation is likely to be lighter.*

ALTITUDE IN FEET
35,000

CIRRUS
Entirely of Ice Particles

CIRROCUMULUS
Mackerel Sky
Ice Particles

30,000

CIRROSTRATUS
Ice Particles Form Halos
Around Sun and Moon, Which
Usually Foretell Rain or Snow
Within 24 Hours

25,000

Anvil Head

20,000

ALTOCUMULUS
'Wool-Pack'' Clouds, Bumpy

CUMULONIMBUS
Violent Vertical Currents

15,000

ALTOSTRATUS
High, Gray Sheet Clouds
Often Followed by Rain or
Snow; Windy

STRATOCUMULUS
Rough, Bumpy

10,000

NIMBOSTRATUS
Storm Clouds

RAIN   SNOW

5,000

CUMULUS
Fair Weather Clouds

RAIN, HAIL AND
SQUALL WINDS

STRATUS
High Fog, "Low Ceiling"

Based on "*Atmosphere and Weather Charts*" published by A. J. Nystrom Co.

Figure 11 *A very generalized representation of the forms and elevations of the principal cloud types.*

weather. On the other hand, when they are systematically arranged in the form of bands and streamers, or when connected with cirrostratus or altostratus, they commonly are harbingers of approaching bad weather. The old proverb of the sailors, "Mackerel scales and mare's-tails make lofty ships carry low sails," has real merit.

2. *Cirrocumulus* exists in the form of patches of white flakes, or of globular masses, usually very small and without shadows. The cloudlets are arranged in groups or lines or more often in ripples. They form the so-called "mackerel sky."

3. *Cirrostratus* is a thin whitish veil of cloud which gives the sky a milky appearance. They do not cast a shadow and are never thick enough to obscure the sun. Halos around the sun or moon usually result from cirrostratus. Commonly they are signs of an approaching storm.

FAMILY B: MIDDLE CLOUDS
(6,500 TO 20,000 FT.)

4. *Altocumulus* are flattened globular masses of clouds arranged in a layer. A patternful distribution, in the form of lines or waves, is common. They differ from cirrocumulus in consisting of larger patches, with definite dark shadings underneath.

5. *Altostratus* is a sheet cloud of gray or bluish color, frequently showing a striated or fibrous structure. It is like thick cirrostratus and often merges gradually with it. Although occasionally and in spots it is thick enough to obscure the sun and moon completely, usually they are able to shine through it, although only wanly and with a faint gleam. Altostratus commonly is followed by widespread precipitation of a relatively continuous type.

FAMILY C: LOW CLOUDS
(FROM CLOSE TO EARTH'S SURFACE
UP TO 6,500 FT.)

6. *Stratocumulus* is composed of large globular masses or rolls of cloud with brighter spaces between. The cloud masses usually are regularly arranged, as in altocumulus, but they are much larger. They are dull gray in appearance, with darker parts.

7. *Stratus* is a low, uniformly gray layer of cloud, resembling fog, but not resting on the ground. It is capable of producing only light drizzle.

8. *Nimbostratus* is a dense, shapeless, and often ragged layer of low clouds, from which precipitation is likely to fall. However, it is not necessary for precipitation to be actually falling in order for the cloud to be classified as nimbostratus. It is darker than stratus, has no well-defined lower surface, and its elements are not regularly arranged as they are in stratocumulus.

FAMILY D: CLOUDS WITH
VERTICAL DEVELOPMENT
(1,600 FT. TO CIRRUS LEVEL)

9. *Cumulus* is a vertically thick cloud with a dome-shaped cauliflower top and a horizontal base. When seen from the sun side they exhibit great contrasts in light and shadow. When seen against the sun they appear dark and ominous, although they may have bright edges. Cumulus clouds are evidence of strong vertical convection currents, and this upsurge of air is visible in the "boiling" of the tops. Much cumulus cloud is of the fair-weather type, although sometimes they grow so high that they become cumulonimbus and produce precipitation of the thunderstorm type.

10. *Cumulonimbus* are overgrown cumulus which have reached such a height that they lose their clear-cut cauliflower shape. They often spread out on top and become anvil-shaped. Such clouds are associated with sharp showers, squall winds, lightning and thunder, and sometimes hail.

Precipitation

ORIGIN

Although all precipitation originates in clouds, by no means do all clouds yield precipitation. It appears that some process other than just condensation in cloud form is required in order for precipitation to result. The reason why many, or even most, clouds do not yield precipitation is that condensation occurs around almost innumerable hygroscopic nuclei and the resulting cloud particles are so tiny that their buoyancy prevents them from falling to earth as rain. The precipitation process, therefore, requires the combining of the myriads of these almost microscopic cloud droplets into a smaller number of larger units capable of falling to earth. A good-sized raindrop may contain as much water as 8 million cloud particles and it falls 200 times as fast.

It is believed that this combining of cloud droplets to form raindrops is the result of two processes. One of these is the ascent of the cloudy air above freezing level where some of the liquid droplets are changed to ice. These ice particles then become very active nuclei around which the cloud water particles combine to form larger raindrops. The second precipitation mechanism is the collision and resulting coalescing of the cloud droplets as they fall at different velocities in the cloud.

FORMS OF PRECIPITATION

Rain, which is much the commonest and most widespread form of precipitation, may be the result of cloud condensation in ascending air at temperatures above freezing. However, some of the earth's rain certainly was originally ice and snow particles, having been formed at temperatures below 32°, which subsequently melted as they fell through the warmer atmosphere closer to the earth's surface.

The most common form of solid precipitation is *snow*. Its fundamental form is the intricately branched, flat, six-sided crystal in an almost infinite variety of patterns. Numerous crystals matted together comprise a snowflake. Snow must develop from condensation which occurs at temperatures below freezing. On the other hand, it may originate in a cloud of supercooled water droplets or it may result from the direct sublimation of ice crystals from water vapor. On the average it requires about 1 ft. of snow to equal 1 in. of rain. Data on the amount and distribution of snowfall are very scant for much of the earth. Snow falls near sea level occasionally in subtropical latitudes but it does not remain on the ground; farther equatorward it is recorded only at relatively high elevations. At low elevations, a durable snow cover in winter lasting for a month or more is characteristic only of the interior and eastern parts of Eurasia and North America poleward from about 40°. In low and middle latitudes a *permanent* snow cover is characteristic only of elevated areas and the height of the snow line declines poleward. Thus while in the deep tropics permanent snow is found at elevations usually over 15,000 ft., at 60°N. in Norway snow remains on the ground throughout the year at an elevation of about 3,500 ft.

Other forms of solid precipitation are sleet and hail. They occur only very occasionally and are restricted in their distribution so that their total climatic significance is minor. Sleet is frozen raindrops. Hail, which falls almost exclusively in violent thunderstorms, is ice lumps which are larger than sleet.

Types of Precipitation Classified According to the Cause of Air Ascent

Almost all of the earth's precipitation originates in ascending air which is adiabatically cooled. It is essential, therefore, to an understanding of the world distribution of precipitation to be familiar with the causes for the ascent of thick and extensive masses of air. Three main types of atmospheric lifting, and their associated precipitation, will be noted. It must be stressed, however, that none of these three usually exists in pure form. They are not mutually exclusive, but on the contrary are characteristically intermingled so that any particular unit of precipitation is commonly the result of the joint action of more than one type of atmospheric lifting.

CONVECTIONAL PRECIPITATION

As a result of the heating of surface air it expands and is forced to rise by the cooler, heavier air above and around it. Ordinarily such rising air, since it cools at nearly double the rate of the normal vertical temperature decrease, will rise only a few thousand feet before its temperature has been reduced to the point where it is the same as that of the surrounding air. At that point where the rising air reaches air strata of its own temperature and density, further ascent ceases. But if abundant condensation begins before this stage is reached, then heat of condensation is released, so that, with this added source of energy, the rising air will be forced to ascend much higher before reaching atmospheric strata of its own temperature. Thus on a hot, humid summer afternoon, when surface heating is intense and condensation abundant, the towering cumulonimbus clouds resulting from convectional ascent may be several miles in vertical depth, and precipitation from them may be copious. Convectional ascent due to simple diurnal surface heating is largely restricted to land areas and is associated with the warmer seasons and with the warm hours of the day. Clearing toward evening is characteristic.

Thermal convection does not consist of the lifting of a widespread air mass, but rather it is in the form of local ascending and descending currents of relatively small horizontal dimensions. Consequently the cumulonimbus clouds associated with the ascending currents are not of great horizontal extent, so that each appears to be single and isolated and there is frequently clear sky between the individual cumuli. Because the cumulonimbus cloud is not extensive in character, the rainfall associated with it is usually of short duration. We speak of it as a thunder *shower* rather than as a thunder *rain*. Since convectional ascent is essentially a vertical movement of warm humid air, cooling is rapid and the associated rainfall is likely to be vigorous.

Because convectional rain commonly comes in the form of heavy showers, it is less effective for crop growth, since much of it, instead of entering the soil, runs off in the form of surface drainage. This is a genuine menace to plowed fields, since soil removal through slope wash and gullying is likely to be serious. On the other hand, for the middle and higher latitudes, convectional rain, since it occurs in the warm season of the year when vegetation is active and crops are growing, comes at the most opportune time. Moreover, it provides the maximum rainfall with the minimum amount of cloudiness. Convectional showers resulting from surface heating are associated with warm regions and warm seasons. This type of rain reaches its maximum development in the wet tropics where heat and humidity conditions are relatively ideal for promoting local convection.

Of a somewhat different origin is rainfall resulting from the overrunning of warm and less dense air by colder, denser currents aloft. When this occurs, atmospheric overturning is likely, the cool, heavy air sinking to the earth and forcing the warm air upward, often violently. Heavy downpours may result.

Still another type of convectional precipitation is associated with humid air masses for which the initial upward thrust is provided by some obstacle such as a mountain range, or a cold wedge of air in a cyclonic storm, or where a simple horizontal convergence of air results in forced ascent. When condensation begins, so much heat of condensation may be added to the non-buoyant ascending air that it eventually becomes unstable and buoyant, and convective ascent then carries it on to greater heights with convectional showers resulting. Such rain is a combination of orographic and convectional or of cyclonic and convectional. It is significant that cumulus clouds and convectional showers are most numerous in regions of horizontal convergence and in mountainous areas.

OROGRAPHIC PRECIPITATION

Large masses of air may be forced to rise when landform barriers, such as mountain ranges, plateau escarpments, or even high hills, lie athwart the paths of winds. Since water vapor is largely confined to the lower layers of atmosphere and rapidly decreases in amount upward, heavy orographic rainfall is the result of such forced ascent of air, associated with the blocking effect of landform obstacles. Witness, for example, the very abundant precipitation along the western or windward flanks of the Cascade Mountains in Washington and Oregon, along parts of the precipitous east coast of Brazil, which lies in the trades, or bordering the abrupt west coast of India, which the summer monsoon meets practically at right angles. The *leeward* sides of such mountain barriers, where the air is descending and warming, are characteristically drier (figure 12). This is called the *rain shadow*. The blocking effect of a mountain is normally felt at some distance out in front of the abrupt change in slope, the approaching wind riding up over a

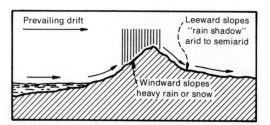

Figure 12 *Precipitation conditions on the windward and leeward slopes of highlands.*

mass of stagnant air along its front. The most ideal condition for producing heavy orographic rainfall is when a high and relatively continuous mountain barrier lies close to a coast and the winds from off a warm ocean meet the barrier at right angles. Orographic rains have less seasonal and daily periodicity than do those of convectional origin. In monsoon regions, very naturally, the maximum is at the time when air is moving from sea to land, usually high sun, or summer. In other regions the strength of the winds, the angle at which they meet the mountain barrier, or the contrast between land and water temperatures may determine the season of maximum orographic rainfall.

It seems likely that a considerable part of the precipitation associated with highlands is not the result of direct forced ascent of the prevailing winds, in other words, not purely orographic in type. Certainly of great importance are such indirect effects as (*a*) the production of convectional currents up mountain slopes exposed to strong isolational heating; (*b*) the "pinching" or "blocking" effect upon cyclonic storms; (*c*) orographically produced convergence in horizontal currents; and (*d*) the providing of a "trigger" effect that gives the initial upthrust to conditionally unstable air masses. Sometimes only a slight amount of lifting is necessary to bring these air masses to condensation level, after which they become unstable and so continue to rise, yielding abundant rainfall. Thus highlands of less than 3,000-ft. elevation, although perhaps inducing no great amount of direct orographic precipitation, may by these indirect means become much rainier areas than the surrounding lowlands.

PRECIPITATION RESULTING FROM
HORIZONTAL CONVERGENCE
(CYCLONIC AND FRONTAL)

In any zone or area of horizontal wind convergence, an upward movement of air must result. Commonly this ascent is not the rapid vertical type, but rather is a more gradual, oblique ascent as along the slope of a mildly inclined plane (figure 13). In the heart of the tropics the converging air masses may be relatively similar in temperature and hence in density. But outside the tropics convergence usually produces a conflict between air masses of contrasting temperature and density, with the colder, denser air providing the obstacle over which the warmer lighter air is forced to ascend. The boundary between the unlike air masses is called a *front*.

Some of the commonest convergence areas of the earth are those associated with moving atmospheric disturbances in the form of pressure waves, troughs, and low-pressure centers called cyclonic storms. In parts of the earth these disturbances are so numerous that on mean pressure and wind charts their paths appear as average lines of convergence. The zone of convergence between the trades (I.T.C.) and those in the North Atlantic and North Pacific lows in winter may be partly of this origin. Thus the designation *cyclonic* or *frontal* precipitation is somewhat, although not completely, synonymous with precipitation associated with horizontal convergence.

Since in cyclones and along their fronts the air commonly is rising obliquely over mildly inclined surfaces of colder air, the cooling of the rising air is less rapid than is the case in vertical convectional currents.

As a result of the slower ascent and cooling, precipitation in cyclones is characteristically less violent than in thunderstorms and is inclined to be steadier and longer continued. The dull, gray, overcast skies and drizzly precipitation of the cooler months in middle latitudes, producing some of the most unpleasant weather of those seasons, are usually associated with cyclones. These storms and their associated fronts are most numerous and best developed during the cool seasons. Where they dominate weather conditions, therefore, they tend to produce fall or winter maxima in precipitation curves. Most of the winter precipitation of lowlands in the middle latitudes is cyclonic or frontal in origin. By no means all the precipitation in a convergent system is of the mild and prolonged type, however, for not infrequently the initial upthrust of air along a front is sufficient to make it unstable so that intermittent showery rain may result.

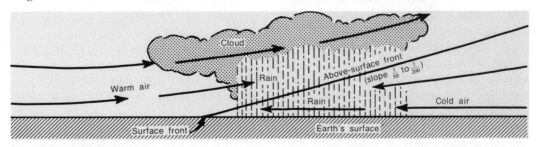

Figure 13 *Precipitation along a front. Here the warmer and less dense air cools due to expansion as it ascends over a wedge of cooler, denser air.*

IMPORTANT FEATURES OF
PRECIPITATION

A satisfactory description of precipitation characteristics for the earth as a whole or for any of its regions involves not only the average total *annual amount,* but also the *seasonal distribution, reliability, intensity,* and *probability* of the rainfall. It is estimated that if the total annual rainfall were spread evenly over the earth's surface it would form a layer about 39 in. deep. Actually precipitation is spread very unevenly, for there are extensive areas that receive less than 5 in. and there are a few spots with over 400 in.

Seasonal distribution of precipitation is coequal in importance with amount. Geographically speaking, the fact that Omaha, Neb., receives 30 in. of rainfall annually is no more significant than the fact that 17.4 in. (58 per cent) falls during the months from May to August and only 3.3 in. (11 per cent) falls during the period November to February. Seasonal distribution of precipitation becomes of greatest importance in the middle latitudes where there is a dormant season for plant growth imposed by low temperatures, *i.e.,* the winter season. In the tropics where frost is practically unknown except at higher elevations, rainfall is effective for plant growth no matter at what time of year it falls. In the middle latitudes, however, only that proportion of the annual precipitation which falls during the frost-free season may be called effective. In the more severe climates a strong concentration of rainfall in the warmer months when plants can use it is desirable.

The dependability or reliability of the annual or seasonal precipitation is an expression of its variability. Data on rainfall reliability are scarcely less important than those concerned with amount and seasonal distribution. Variability may be defined as the deviation from the mean computed from 35 years or more of observations. In humid climates the annual variability is usually not greater than 50 per cent on either side of the mean, *i.e.* the driest year may have about 50 per cent of the normal value while the wettest year may have 150 per cent. In dry climates these values vary between about 30 and 250 per cent. It is a general rule that variability increases as the amount of rainfall decreases. It is an inverse ratio. Variability of precipitation must be taken into consideration when agricultural plans are made, for it must be expected that there will be years when the precipitation is less than the average. In semiarid and subhumid climates where crop raising normally depends on a small margin of safety, rainfall variability is of utmost concern. Moreover, the agriculturist in such regions must bear in mind that negative deviations from the mean are more frequent than positive ones, which indicates that a greater number of dry years are compensated for by a few excessively wet ones. Variability of seasonal and monthly rainfall amounts is even greater than for annual values.

Intensity and Probability. There are many other types of useful precipitation data, although most of them are probably of less value than the three mentioned previously. For example the number of rainy days (defined as one having at least 0.01 in. of rainfall) compared with the total amount of annual rainfall is an indication of the way the rain falls, or its *intensity.* At London, England, the annual rainfall of about 25 in. is spread over 164 rainy days which indicates a lower intensity than the conditions at Cherrapunji, India, where 440 in. falls in 159 days. The *probability* of rainy days offers a kind of information that has considerable value to such people as farmers and resort owners. This may be readily computed by dividing the number of rainy days in a month or a year by the total number of days.

VII

THE ATMOSPHERE OF the young earth must have been the breeding ground of violent atmospheric disturbances. Certainly since the first appearance of thinking life, storms have been a source of wonder. Man has been intrigued for centuries by the phenomena of the earth's atmosphere—thunderstorms, howling gales and lashing rains. Scientists have only recently found that our atmosphere is like a soup steaming in a great kettle, boiled and roiled by radiant heat from the sun.

The greatest advances in weather science have been made since 1946. Modern electronic devices, weather balloons, satellites and rockets are supplying unique observations of atmospheric activity. High-speed electronic computers analyze vast quantities of data in a short time and allow easy solutions to complex equations dealing with atmospheric motions.

Louis J. Battan, professor of meteorology at the University of Arizona, has been associated with research on storms for more than fifteen years. In the following selection, he records some pertinent information about weather study and the necessary ingredients for storm formation.

Storms

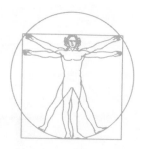

METEOROLOGY is one branch of science in which almost everyone may participate. People who work out-of-doors soon develop firm ideas on weather forecasting. Certain cloud types and wind directions mean it will rain; others mean it will not rain. Even the old-fashioned housewife who hung her clothes on the line in the back yard was prepared to match her skills with the Weather Bureau. Many of the unwritten rules of the laymen are correct, of course. The extreme conditions, perfectly clear or very rainy, are frequently quite easy to predict if the time period is short. The real problem of the weather forecaster is to be able to predict all types of weather and to do it accurately one or more days in advance. When forecasts go sour, the reasons can almost always be found in a lack of understanding of the physical processes involved, not only by the forecasters but by meteorologists in general. The unknowns in meteorology probably outnumber the knowns. Furthermore, every question answered usually produces many more questions of equal or greater interest and importance.

Among the fascinating problems confronting meteorologists are those dealing with thunderstorms, tornadoes, and other vortices in the atmosphere. The winds in such storms may vary from gusts of low speeds to whirls of air spinning at several hundreds of miles per hour. Great losses of life and property occur every year whenever violent vortices strike unsuspecting communities. Scientists have constantly sought better descriptions of storm structures and explanations for their formation. After decades of effort a great deal has been learned, not nearly enough, of course, but at least there is enough known to make useful forecasts and intelligently plan new research.

Intense vortices in the atmosphere can be taken as signs that the atmosphere is unstable and has high moisture contents. These ingredients are necessary in order to supply the huge quantities of energy needed to start and maintain the circulating air. It is easy to fail to appreciate the total power of a storm because one experiences only a small part at any one time. However, estimates of the energy involved in various weather systems can be made fairly easily if the size of the system and the wind speeds are known. Table 1 gives estimates of the *kinetic energy* of the weather systems. The kinetic energy, for those not familiar with the term, is that energy represented by the motion of the air. In order to stop the air altogether, one would have to expend the same amount of energy. It should be noted that the numbers apply to an average storm. In any particular case the amount of energy may be somewhat larger or smaller than the amount shown in the table.

TABLE 1. Order of magnitude estimates of the kinetic energy of various wind sytems and of atomic and hydrogen bombs expressed in kilowatt-hours.

SYSTEM	KINETIC ENERGY*
Gust	Less than 1
Dust Devil	10
Tornado	10^4
Thunderstorm	10^6
Hurricane	10^{10}
Cyclone	10^{11}
Nagasaki Atom Bomb	10^7
Hydrogen Bomb	10^{10}

*The superscript refers to the number of zeros after the one. For example, 10^4 means 10,000 and 10^6 means 1,000,000.

By any scale of measure it is obvious that weather systems are powerful. This becomes even more striking when one realizes that the amount of energy input required to develop these kinetic energies is 10 to 100 times greater than the tabulated values. The major portion of the energy in atmospheric systems is expended in overcoming the effects of friction and in heating the air inside and outside the systems. It can readily be seen that the input energy to an average hurricane may be equivalent to more than 10,000 atomic bombs of the kind that destroyed Nagasaki.

The reason storms such as cyclones and hurricanes do not do more damage is that the energy is distributed over a large region. In a tornado, on the other hand, it may be concentrated over an area 100 yards wide. Then explosive effects occur.

The numbers in the table also clearly indicate that man will find it difficult to modify the weather by competing with nature on the energy field-of-battle. If one were to try to produce cyclones by supplying the necessary energy, the efforts would be in vain. One could do it with hydrogen bombs but the radioactivity would make the consequences disastrous. If we are to succeed in attempts to modify large-scale weather systems, it will first be necessary to find unstable regions which can be influenced by small energy changes. We must find the equivalent of the delicately balanced boulder, which is too heavy to carry, but which will roll down the mountain if given a small push. This area of meteorology is a fascinating one and permits much speculation. . . .

There are various sources of energy for atmospheric vortices. Heat contained in the air and earth's surface and the sinking of heavier air when it moves over lighter air are important factors. But the major contribution comes from heat released when water vapor condenses to form clouds. R. R. Braham, Jr., at the University of Chicago, has shown that in a single thunderstorm about 3 miles in diameter, there may be 500,000 tons of condensed water in the form of water droplets and ice crystals. In the course of producing these particles, there would have been released about 3×10^{14} calories. This is equal to about 10^8 kw-hrs or about 100 times greater than the value of the estimated kinetic energy given in table 1.

Tornadoes are associated with thunderstorms and apparently derive their energy from them. In hurricanes and cyclones there are widespread areas of cloudiness and rainfall. They indicate the release of enormous quantities of heat of condensation.

When the humidity of the air is very low, relatively small quantities of energy are available for conversion into kinetic energy. Nevertheless, vortices still develop. They may be seen as dust devils over the arid regions of the world. These whirls sometimes become large enough to blow down wooden shacks or unhinge screen doors, but they fall far short of a tornado.

The important prerequisite for the formation of a dust devil is a high temperature at the earth's surface. When this condition is combined with an air flow which has a certain amount of curvature, the whirls of the desert are a common sight. When the earth is very hot, the overlying air always is affected. Dust devils are markers of unusual activity because dust is carried upward and can be seen. If a small airplane is flown within several thousand feet of the hot terrain, the effects of the heating become dramatically evident as turbulence, even when no dust is present. Air in the lowest layers heats up, becomes lighter and rises. When an airplane passes through a parcel of ascending air it is carried upward. If the air ascends in a certain region, you usually can expect air to be descending in a nearby region. As a result, an airplane constantly experiences upward and downward accelerations. In this situation the air has a very gusty character and is said to be turbulent.

Quite evidently air motions in the atmosphere cover a wide range of sizes and intensities from weak gusts amounting to a few feet per minute to extreme updrafts with speeds of several miles per minute. The winds in the atmosphere can vary from a mile per hour or less around a large high-pressure area to several hundred miles per hour around a circle having a diameter of several hundred yards. The duration of the unusual winds can vary from gusts which last only a few seconds to vortices which last for days. Dimensions of the various phenomena also have a large range, extending from gusts of a few feet or so to hurricanes and cyclones more than 1000 miles in diameter. . . .

Regions of Cyclone Formation and Cyclone Movements

Unlike hurricanes, which always form over warm oceans, middle latitude cyclones may form over land or sea. As a matter of fact, they may form virtually anywhere along the polar front. However, there are certain favored breeding grounds.

Over North America, cyclones frequently form just to the east of the Rocky Mountains. This fact has led many to the conclusion that the storms are initiated, at least in part, by the effects of the mountains. The average path taken by these vortices is slightly toward the east-southeast and then north of east. These are the storms that sweep across the central and northeastern United States and bring blizzards and cold weather.

Many cyclones form in the Gulf of Mexico and follow a track to the northeast along the eastern coast of the United States and then into the northern part of the Atlantic Ocean. Cyclones that strike northern Europe often are initiated over these same Atlantic waters. Storms affecting the Mediterranean region frequently come into being in the vicinity of Spain and move eastward.

Over the Pacific Ocean there are several favorite spawning areas. Many vortices develop over the ocean to the east and south of Japan and then tend to follow a northeast track. Cyclones often form over

Siberia and move toward the east over the Islands of Japan and bring severe weather and cold waves.

Cyclones that strike the western coasts of North America form along the polar front running across the northern part of the Pacific Ocean. Many also begin over the ocean several thousand miles west of California. When these storms strike the west coast of the United States, they are often in an advanced stage of development. They bring rainfalls of major importance to the economy of the western states.

If you plot the tracks followed by cyclones, you see that on the average they move from southwest to northeast. There are at least two important factors governing the movements. The cyclones form as

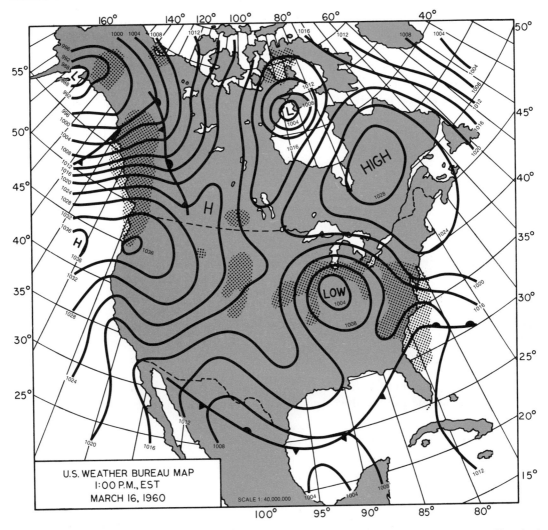

U.S. WEATHER BUREAU MAP
1:00 P.M., EST
MARCH 16, 1960

SCALE 1: 40,000,000

The official U. S. Weather Bureau map for 1:00 p.m. on March 16, 1960, shows several cyclones. The shaded areas represent regions of precipitation. The map shows rain along the east and west coasts and snow over the central parts of the continent. Twenty-four hours earlier the cyclone shown over Illinois on the map was over Oklahoma. A young wave is forming along the Carolina coast.

waves, which tend to move up the south-west-northeast oriented polar front. Such behavior is specified by the polar-front theory of cyclones. It has also been found that the cyclones tend to be "steered" by the prevailing winds at the middle and high altitudes. These winds on the average move from the west or southwest in the regions where cyclones are found.

It is well to keep in mind that most cyclones do not exactly follow the average paths mentioned in the preceding paragraphs. One major factor involved is the position of the polar front. In the winter it is farther south than in the summer, and the storms form at lower latitudes during the cold season of the year. Also, the "steering currents" usually deviate somewhat from the average pattern.

Individual cyclones differ from one another in many respects. Some have circular patterns of pressure, but most are elliptical with the longest axis in the north-south direction. Some may develop in a matter of hours; others may take days. Some may remain almost stationary for many hours, while others may move across the country at speeds of perhaps 40 or 50 miles per hour. On the average the speeds are 20 miles per hour in the summer and 30 miles per hour in the winter.

A single well-developed cyclone may dominate the weather for many days and then move off the continent, to be followed by an anticyclone and fair weather. Again, cyclones may form in rapid succession in the same area over a period of one or two weeks. Such a situation can lead to prolonged periods of bad weather broken by short periods of clear skies.

The weather over most of the eastern half of the United States during March of 1960 was caused by this kind of situation. Cyclone after cyclone formed just east of the Rocky Mountains and moved toward the east and in the process dropped huge quantities of snow (figure 1). With each succeeding storm, the snow piled higher and created many records for the amount measured in one year.

The differences from one cyclone to another must be faced by the weather forecaster virtually every day. In order to make accurate predictions of temperature and rainfall he must predict the formation, intensification, and movement of cyclones. Until a few years ago this was done with forecasting rules that involved rather elementary types of calculations, and the accuracy of the forecasts depended to a large extent on the experience of the forecaster. Today, more and more use is being made of high-speed electronic computers, which in short periods of time, can make calculations from the complex equations describing the air motion over a large part of the Northern Hemisphere. This modern approach to atmospheric problems promises better understanding of the weather and, ultimately, better forecasts.

VIII

IN THE EARLY DAYS of aviation, it was not at all unusual for an unfortunate airplane venturing into a mighty thunderstorm to come out one piece at a time. Violent air motions, lightning and hail frightened the bravest pilots.

Aviation grew in popularity and practicality, and more planes were manufactured and flown. An increased knowledge of thunderstorms became necessary as more and more pilots and planes were lost in turbulent thunderstorm cloud formations.

The list of questions to be answered was a long one. How strong were the air currents? How strong must a plane be to survive the air turbulence? How could pilots avoid turbulent regions? What were the best flight altitudes? What could be done if a pilot found himself in a thunderstorm? But research produced few answers until radar was developed during World War II.

In the following selection, the noted meteorologist, Louis J. Battan, discusses the role of radar in helping to solve some of aviation's weather problems.

Radar Observes the Weather

IN THE cockpit of an airliner the pilot is quietly calculating the best course of action. The airplane is engulfed in a heavy cloud mass. The wing tips are not even visible, but periodically one can see a red glow caused by the blinking lights on the wing tips.

Thirty minutes ago the air had been smooth, but now the situation is rapidly becoming unpleasant. At frequent intervals the airplane bounces and shakes, indicating increasingly turbulent conditions. The seat belt sign is on. Every so often flashes of lightning light up the sky.

Some of the passengers who have flown a great deal are listening to the sounds of the engines and mentally flying the airplane. They reduce the air speed to minimize the effects of the air gusts and strain their eyes staring into the mist to see if they can spot the thunderstorms buried in the clouds. The cloud droplets and poor visibility are no cause for alarm. The danger is concentrated in the thunderstorms, where updrafts or downdrafts of several thousand feet per minute are waiting to lift or drop the air-

plane like a leaf and shake it violently— where hailstones and lightning are also waiting to strike.

Not many years ago even the good pilots feared the thunderstorm, but now the situation has changed. Yesterday's aviator had to rely on experience and luck to get him through without giving himself and the passengers a good scare. The biggest problem was to locate the thunderstorm regions which harbored the severe weather. When the aircraft is in clouds, it is impossible to see these regions. Today we have a gadget which can "see" through clouds. The pilot of today's airliner has, as part of his flying aids, a radar set which can spot thunderstorms far out ahead of him.

As the airplane penetrates a wall of clouds and moves closer to the region of treacherous weather, the pilot sees it mapped out on a radarscope. After watching for a short time, he can calculate his best course of action. Should he go straight ahead and pick his way between storms by making only slight deviations in airplane heading? Should he begin a long swing

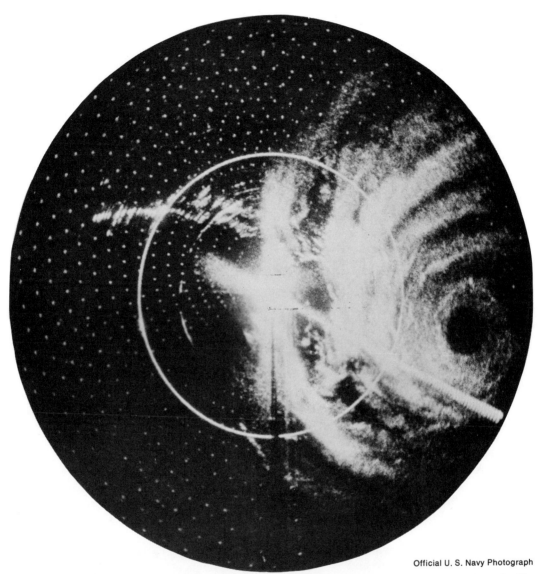

Official U. S. Navy Photograph

A U. S. Navy "Hurricane Hunter" plane took this radar photo of a destructive hurricane named Gracie. The circular storm pattern swirls over parts of three southeastern states.

around the storm area? Now that he knows where the storms are he can answer these questions. As a result, airplane travel has become safer and, of course, much more comfortable. And the equipment known as radar not only has been an aid to airline travel but has become a standard observational instrument at many weather stations and is used extensively by weather scientists.

What is radar? How does it work? What can it do to improve weather observations? What can it tell us about the ways of the atmosphere?

The word radar came from the term "radio detection and ranging," that is, the use of radio waves to detect objects and to measure the distances to them. Without doubt, radar was one of the outstanding electronic developments that came out of World War II.

Quite clearly, it was of the utmost importance during the war to be able to accurately locate and track enemy airplanes and ships in all types of weather and at any time, day or night. For bombing from airplanes it was essential to be able to locate targets hidden under layers of clouds. Tremendous efforts were devoted to the development of a system which could accomplish these purposes.

Early in the war, in England and other countries under frequent air attacks, widespread use was made of powerful search lights which would seek airplanes in the sky. Although this scheme was quite useful on nights with clear skies, it was a failure when the sky was covered with clouds or when fogs and haze shrouded the ground. Sound ranging techniques also had been used for locating aircraft, but they had many disadvantages. Sound travels at speeds of only about 700 mph and is subject to many deviations in speed and direction by the atmosphere. Sound equipment is still used for detecting underwater vehicles such as submarines, but for aircraft it has been completely abandoned.

For detection of objects on the earth's surface or in the air, radar is far superior to the visual or acoustical methods. It can function over a large range of conditions. It makes no difference whether it is day or night, and ordinary clouds and fog usually do not seriously affect radar. If one wishes, it is possible to detect targets at very great distances as well as very close ones. For these reasons, radar was used extensively during the last war in nearly all

phases of ground, naval, and air operations. Since then more powerful and versatile equipment has been built. . . .

Over the past fifteen years, meteorologists have learned a great deal about clouds and precipitation. Many of the mysteries of thunderstorms, tornadoes, and cyclones have been uncovered. Radar has played an important role in this progress. Along with the instrumented airplane, capable of making detailed measurements in the free air, radar brought to the hands of atmospheric scientists large quantities of new observations to permit better descriptions of many kinds of weather phenomena.

Another instrumental triumph of the last twenty years, the high-speed electronic computer, has made it possible to solve some of the complex equations that describe atmospheric processes and predict future weather. The computer has helped to unravel problems that would have been completely unmanageable in the forties.

Probably the most important development in meteorology in the last two decades has been the rise in the number of highly competent scientists who have joined in the study of the atmosphere. The great advances in all aspects of this, or any other, science are a measure of the competence of the people involved. In the last few years, with the successful launching of artificial satellites, especially the Tiros series of weather satellites, the atmospheric sciences have received added impetus. As these new techniques solve old questions, they create many new and exciting ones. The need for daring and imagination was never so great, the benefits never so satisfying.

As MAN FLIES HIGHER and higher, he finds atmospheric phenomena which he must understand before he can fly safely at high altitudes. Military and commercial jet aircraft have been flying safely at high altitudes for some time. But now, even some private aircraft are equipped for operation in the upper troposphere and lower stratosphere.

Pilots flying at altitudes of four to nine miles above the earth are sometimes confronted with a band of variable winds. Among the swiftest known, these winds are called *jet streams*. With velocities sometimes reaching 400 miles an hour, the jet streams do not blow steadily, but vary in speed, direction and extent. These narrow, shallow, meandering rivers of strong wind seem to have a cycle of formation, increased intensity, movement and dissipation related to the polar front.

Early encounters with the jet stream were disastrous. Since then we have learned that a jet stream's orientation, zones of greatest wind, location and depth generally vary with longitude, latitude, time and altitude. In winter they are only four to six miles high, but in summer months they soar to heights that only experimental aircraft can reach. Flying the jet streams is becoming more common, however, as information about their habits is accumulated.

In the selection that follows, Theo Loebsack, German meteorologist, gives a lucid account of these atmospheric jet streams.

The Jet-Stream

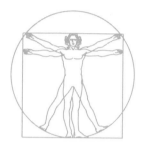

OF ALL THE gales and storms on this planet, man has only been able to subjugate, or rather make use of, a single one. Flyers call this wind the "gulf stream of the air," because its typical shape is that of a tube stretching across the sky. It is called the jet-stream, and its discovery resembles an adventure story.

On a sunny day in 1944 a long-distance American B.29 bomber droned across the Pacific Ocean. The crew, experienced, reliable airmen, were briefed to attack a target in Japan. The weather forecast had promised good flight conditions and nothing seemed to stand in their way.

As they left the mainland a feeling of anxiety gripped the pilot and spread to the whole crew. At first they believed that their senses deceived them, but their doubts soon vanished, for something was definitely holding their machine back. An invisible hand seemed to be tugging at the stern of the aeróplane and, although all the engines were at full throttle, the B.29 was only moving forwards with difficulty. A group of islands that they had passed quickly on previous flights remained in their field of vision for an exceptionally long time; finally the bomber almost stood still in the air.

What had happened? The B.29 had flown into a jet-stream, one of those treacherous tube-shaped air zones in which the wind blows from west to east at tremendous speeds. The bomber's engines fought in vain against this hurricane-like storm of the upper air. The pilot did not reach his target that day, but had to return home after dropping his load of bombs harmlessly into the sea.

Whilst the United States Air Force was having its first experience of the jet-stream, the Japanese already had some knowledge of these mysterious currents. They knew, for instance, that a fairly constant high wind blew from their islands to the American West Coast, and they even made use of it during the last months of the war. Under the direction of General Kusaba, Japanese technicians constructed special balloons, which were intended to set fire to the American forests, after being carried over the ocean by the jet-stream.

No less than 9000 balloons started out for the American West Coast during the "balloon offensive" in the spring of 1944 and winter 1944-45. It was a major offensive, if one considers that each balloon cost about £200, and it was also a major technical achievement. During the flight of about 2500 miles an ingenious mechanism kept the balloons at a height between 29,000 and 36,000 feet, just where the meteorologists had found the jet-stream. The control of height was cleverly managed: a barometer worked the release which dropped one of thirty little sandbags whenever the balloon sank below 29,000 feet. If it rose higher than 36,000 feet, a valve released some of the hydrogen which lifted the balloon. Accompanying control balloons carried short-wave equipment, and sent back reports on their position at certain intervals, so that the whereabouts of the flotilla could be checked.

We know now that only about nine hundred balloons (or ten per cent) reached the American mainland between Mexico and Alaska. Some of them landed in coastal waters, some of them drifted two hundred and fifty miles inland; some exploded and some started fires, but they caused little damage. The Japanese venture was soon forgotten, but the jet-streams were not, and their importance in modern aerial communications is constantly growing. They have already become what the trade winds once were for sailing ships, a gift from Nature which, correctly used, saves fuel and travelling time.

The riddle of the jet-streams pricked the curiosity of the meteorologists. They pondered the question how Nature manages to create a sudden suction in such a mobile medium as the air, and how it happens that they are narrow, sharply defined zones in which the air races along like a mountain torrent, carrying everything before it?

German meteorologists had already in the nineteen-thirties come across ribbons of exceptionally strong winds at a great height and called them "High Jet Currents," but the first steps toward their explanation were taken by a group of Chicago weather experts. The Americans had sent up balloons to heights where the jet-streams blew, collected reports from other countries and systematically worked towards an explanation. Gradually they built up a picture of the jet-streams which was at least as complete as our knowledge of other aerial conditions, such as those leading to thunderstorms.

It is a matter of fact that jet-streams occur at between 20,000 to 35,000 feet and that their height is greater in summer than in winter. They can attain the fantastic speed of 300 or even more than 370 miles per hour, and preferentially occur in zones of varying width, about 1800 miles from the equator, completely encircling both hemispheres of the globe.

The scientists got a pointer from the fact that the jet-streams occurred particularly in the middle latitudes and travelled mainly from west to east. From this they could deduce that they were perhaps connected with the distribution of temperature over the earth. This proved to be true; wherever the jet-streams blew, warm tropical air met cold polar air.

Let us take an example (figure 1) and imagine a High over the Azores in the Atlantic and two Lows to the west and east of it. Above Iceland in the north there is the centre of another strong Low, which on its part is flanked by Highs on the west (Canada) and east (North Scandinavia). Under such conditions, which are by no means rare, warm air will stream north-east from the edge of the High over the Azores and cold air will flow south-west from the edge of the Low over Iceland. The two air streams will meet approximately over the fiftieth degree of latitude to form a weather-

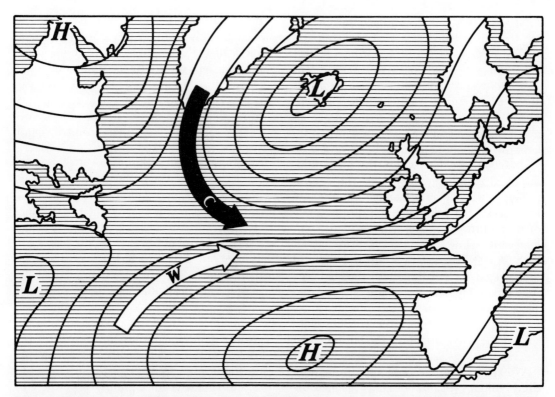

Figure 1 *Under certain conditions jet-streams are formed where warm and cold air masses meet. This map shows a typical jet-stream generating conditions over the Atlantic. Between the High (below center) and the Low (over Iceland) masses of warm (W) and cold (C) air meet.*

front, a region of marked differences of temperature.

The birth place of the jet-stream winds lies in this weather-front at a height of about six miles. Every weather expert knows that there is a strong pressure difference between cold air and warm air at great heights. The air, like any other gas, tries to eliminate this difference and begins to move from the warm to the cold side. If the temperature differential is very great, this movement becomes violent. It is as if two canals ran along a sloping hillside at different heights; if the upper one overflows, the water will run down the hill and collect in the lower one just like the air. on its journey from the warm region (South) to the cold region (North). There is one difference, however: whereas the water will flow from one canal to the other in a direct line, the air that was originally moving from south to north will be deflected by the earth's rotation. If we are in the Northern Hemisphere it will be deflected to the right and the final direction will therefore be from west to east; the jet-stream is born.

The hotter the warm air and the cooler the cold air, the greater will be the pressure difference in high regions. The greater this difference, the greater will be the speed of the jet-stream, which has the strongest turbulence in the centre and less violent winds at its edges.

It is of great importance for a pilot to ascertain quickly if there is a jet-stream in the vicinity of his route, and whether he can count on strong and steady winds. An experienced pilot can often recognise a jet-stream by the typical clouds which accompany it. To the south of it there is usually a layer of feathery, riffled or striated cirrus cloud which runs parallel to the stream and often extends from one end of the horizon to the other. To the north the sky is usually clear and deep blue, while there is often a bank of lenticularis alto-cumulus clouds below the jet-stream itself (these clouds are the same as those seen over mountain peaks during a Föhn, when they glisten in the sun like small pennants of smoke). It is not always possible to make a long-distance diagnosis, however, for sometimes jet-streams occur mysteriously in a clear sky.

If the pilot does not want to trust to luck in his search, he has another method as well, temperature measurement. The temperature is distributed around the jet-stream according to certain laws, and a knowledge of these laws will turn the thermometer into a sort of Geiger-counter. With a little ingenuity the pilot can tell from temperature readings whether he is to the north or south, above or below the jet-stream.

Once the pilot is inside the jet-stream he must navigate carefully so as not to lose it. Modern technology has called in radar, the new "maid-of-all-work," and given the pilot an instrument on which he can read the direction and speed of the stream right away.

The importance of always knowing the exact direction of this moody wind is demonstrated by an ominous fact. It may happen that the jet-stream is forced from its path by a sudden advance of cold polar air,

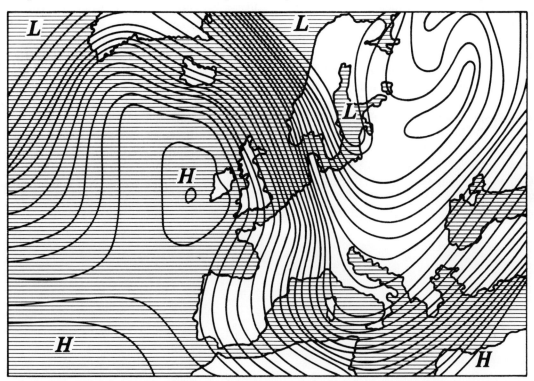

Figure 2 *Was it the fault of the weather? This map shows the distribution of air pressure over Europe on January 10, 1954. The weather expert can deduce from it that a jet-stream blew across the western Mediterranean at a time when the Comet, a British jet plane, met with an accident in that region. In addition to this there was also a "squall-zone."*

in which case "squall-zones" may appear in its immediate neighbourhood. These are regions in which the strength of the wind varies, exposing the aeroplane to dangerously changing loads.

Such squall zones probably played an important part in the incompletely understood disaster of the Comet, the British jet plane which was lost over the Mediterranean on the 10th of January, 1954. A glance at figure 2 will show you the air pressure distribution high over Europe on the day of the accident. The lines, which connect points of equal air pressure, show a distinct concentration over Western Europe. A meteorologist will deduce a strong hurricane band running from high over the North Atlantic via Western Germany and the Western Mediterranean to the North African coast, where it bends eastwards. The jet-stream itself, however, was not the main danger. The decisive point was that warm tropical air (high pressure areas marked H on the left of the map) was pushing from the west to the north-east on the western and eastern side of a sack-shaped wedge of cold air. This led to a squall zone between Rome and Sardinia at a height of about six miles, well within the route of the Comet, which mysteriously disintegrated.

He who wants to "ride the high storm" must be aware of the dangers and know how to avoid them. If this is the case he can go hunting for records, trying to lower the times for long, trans-oceanic flights. Aeroplanes flying from Tokyo to the United States in the jet-stream have already saved about six hours' flying time, and over two thousand gallons of fuel. The American pilot R. P. McManus took a passenger plane from Tokyo to Anchorage (Alaska) in 9 hours and 19 minutes, and this included a stop at the island of Shemya in the Aleutians.

Flights of an equally impressive nature are also possible across the Atlantic and the European mainland, for the ribbon of the jet-stream stretches right round the globe like a meandering river: from the Himalayas via Japan to North America, onward across the Atlantic to Europe and back to Asia. As flying techniques improve the thrust of the jet-stream will be used increasingly, and the feats which only a few pilots can manage today will become a routine job for all tomorrow. Perhaps the factories will turn out aeroplanes which can ride the storm with unpowered flight. This would be an event of which we could say that the dream of the flying carpet has come true.

X

ONE OF THE MOST DRAMATIC and exotic land-shaping forces on earth is volcanism. While our continental United States has had its share of this spectacular activity in the past, the most recent eruption was in the volcanic Cascade range of mountains, when Mount Lassen, California, blew its top in 1915. Since the earth regulates its own time scheme for volcanic activity, with periods of eruption that may be spaced hundreds or thousands of years apart, Lassen cannot yet be considered totally dead. For current drama within our own country, however, we have to look to Hawaii or Alaska.

Many of the world's striking examples of volcanic activity have been in far-off lands. The following selection tells about one of the most famous eruptions in history, the tremendous blowup of Krakatoa. Written by a noted geologist, William C. Putnam, formerly of the Geology Department of the University of California at Los Angeles, this selection describes the spectacular events involved in one type of volcanic activity.

Krakatoa

THREE quarters of a century ago captains of sailing ships beating their way through the Sunda Straits which separate the great islands of Java and Sumatra in the East Indies knew the island of Krakatoa well. Its conical, green-clad slopes rose uninterruptedly about 2,600 feet to the summit of the central peak. The straits were important since they were on the shortest sea road for the tea clippers en route from China to England. These were dangerous, restricted waters, haunted by sea-roving Dyaks who could give the crew of a becalmed vessel a bad time. In this same seaway many years later the U.S.S. *Houston*, harried by pursuing Japanese in the early years of World War II, blew up and sank with the loss of almost all hands.

Though the island of Krakatoa had been spasmodically active since May, 1883, it seemed innocuous enough to the crew of the British ship *Charles Bal*, tacking under all plain sail through the hot tropical Sunday afternoon of August 26, 1883, until they arrived on one heading at a point

about 10 miles south of the island. Minutes later the mountain exploded. Seldom in the long history of seafaring has the crew of any vessel been confronted by such a satanic outburst of energy. The entire mountain disappeared in clouds of black "smoke," and the air was charged with electricity—lightning flashed continuously over the volcano, as it very often does during eruptions, and the yards and rigging of the ship glowed with St. Elmo's fire. Immense quantities of heated ash fell on the deck or hissed through the surrounding darkness into the increasingly disturbed sea. As the vessel labored across broken seas through squalls of mud-laden rain, a thundering roar of explosions continued, much like a never-ending artillery barrage, accompanied by a ceaseless crackling sound which resembled the tearing of gigantic sheets of paper. This last effect was interpreted to be the rubbing together of large rocks hurled skyward by the explosions. After an interminable night, the dawn, dim as it must have been, came as deliverance, and with the coast of Java in view and a gale rising rapidly, the *Charles Bal* was able to set all sail and leave the smoking mountain far astern.

It is well she did, for paroxysms of volcanic fury continued to shake the mountain until the final culmination of four prodigious explosions came on Monday, August 27, at 5:30, 6:44, 10:02, and 10:52 a.m. The greatest of these, the third, was one of the most titanic explosions recorded in modern times—greater in intensity than some of our nuclear efforts. The sound was heard over tremendous distances: at Alice Springs in the heart of Australia, in Manila, in Ceylon, and on the remote island of Rodriguez in the southwest Indian Ocean, where it arrived four hours after the explosion had occurred, 3,000 miles away.

The explosion seriously agitated the Earth's atmosphere, and records of such a disturbance were picked up by barometers all over the world. They showed that a shock wave originating in the East Indies traveled at least seven times around the world—out to the antipodes of the volcano and back again—before it became too faint to register on the instruments of that time.

Visibly, a more impressive phenomenon was the huge cloud of pumice and volcanic debris that blew skyward. The steam-impelled cloud of volcanic ash is estimated to have risen to a height of 50 miles on August 27, and to have blanketed a surrounding area of 300,000 square miles. The ash poured down as a pasty mud on the streets and buildings of Batavia—now Djakarta—83 miles away. Pumice in great floating rafts blanketed much of the Indian Ocean, and captains' comments recorded in logbooks of ships suddenly enmeshed in far-reaching masses of pumice far offshore make interesting reading.

Volcanic ash hurled into the upper levels of the Earth's atmosphere was picked up by the jet stream—whose existence was not even suspected then—and carried with it as a dust cloud that encircled the Earth in the equatorial regions in thirteen days. Incidentally, the jet stream was virtually forgotten, only to be rediscovered in our age of high-altitude flight, jet travel, and radioactive fallout. The ash continued to spread across both hemispheres of the Earth and produced a succession of spectacular and greatly admired sunsets over most of the world—even in areas as remote from Java as England and the northeastern United States—for the two years that it took the finer dust particles to settle through the atmosphere.

The violent explosion of the morning of August 27 set in motion one of the more destructive sea waves ever to be recorded. It spread out in ever-widening circles from Krakatoa much as though a gigantic rock had been hurled into the sea. About half an hour after the eruption, the wave reached the shores of Java and Sumatra, and on these low-lying coasts the water surged inland with a crest whose maximum height was about 120 feet. Since many of the people inhabiting such a densely populated tropical coast lived in houses built on piers extending out over the water, about 30,000 or 40,000 people lost their lives.

The sea wave, after leaving the Sunda Strait with diminishing height, raced on across the open ocean. It was registered long after it was too faint to see, as a train of pulses on recording tide gauges along the coasts of India and Africa and on the coasts of Europe and the western United States. For example, the tide gauges in San Francisco Bay showed a disturbance of about 6 inches by waves that traveled a distance of 10,343 miles at a speed of about 594 miles per hour, a value which seems high. In the Indian Ocean, the velocity of the wave appears to have varied between 200 and 400 miles per hour in the open ocean. This agrees with the better-timed earthquake wave that originated on the coast of Chile and destroyed the low-lying parts of Hilo, Hawaii, on May 23, 1960, 11 hours and 56 minutes later, having traveled 6,600 miles at an average speed of 442 miles per hour (Eaton, 1961).

After the explosions died down returning observers were startled to find that where the 2,600-foot mountain had stood was now a hole whose bottom was 900 to 1,000 feet below sea level, and that the sea now filled this large bowl-shaped depression. All that remained of the island were three tiny islets on the rim. All told, although the estimates vary, a little less than 5 cubic miles of material were hurled into the atmosphere. In popular accounts of the eruption the impression commonly is given that a volcanic mountain blew up and its fragments were strewn far and wide over the face of the Earth. Were this to be the case, we should expect most of the debris covering the little islands which are the surviving remnants of Krakatoa would be pieces of the wrecked volcano, and the oversize crater, or *caldera*, now filled with sea water would be the product of a simple explosion.

Unfortunately for this seemingly plausible explanation, few pieces of the original volcanic mountain are to be found, and instead of such fragments the ground is covered with deposits of pumice up to 200 feet thick. You may also recall in the description of the eruption the mention of the great rafts of floating pumice in the Indian Ocean which were a source of surprise to the mariners who encountered them drifting over much of the open sea. Pumice is original magmatic material, frothed up by gases contained in the magma, and has nothing to do with the internal composition of the vanished mountain. Thus, the abundance of pumice and the absence of pieces of the mountain lead logically to the belief that the volcanic

cone foundered or collapsed on itself rather than having been blown to bits.

The explanation that appears to be correct was advanced by a Dutch volcanologist, van Bemmelen, in 1929, and refined by Howel Williams, of the University of California, in 1941. Figure 1, adapted from Williams, shows the sequence of eruptive events which very likely were responsible for the disappearance of a 2,600-foot mountain and the appearance of a 1,000-foot deep caldera in its place.

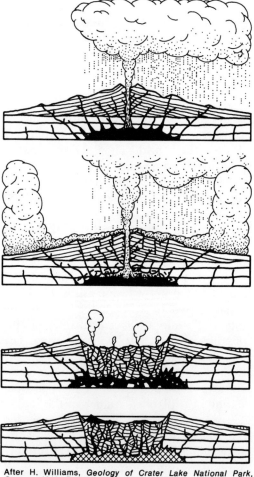

After H. Williams, *Geology of Crater Lake National Park, Oregon*, 1942. By permission of The Carnegie Institution of Washington.

Figure 1 *Stages in the collapse of a volcanic mountain to form a caldera.*

Stage I. The eruptive cycle commenced with fairly mild explosions of pumice. The magma chamber was filled and the magma stood high in the conduits. With an increase in the violence of the explosions, magma was drawn off more and more rapidly and the level dropped in the magma chamber.

Stage II. The culminating explosions cleared out the volcanic conduits and rapidly lowered the magma level in the chamber. In this phase pumice was blown high above the cone, or glowing, pumice-laden clouds swept down the flanks.

Stage III. With removal of support, the volcanic cone collapsed into the magma chamber below, leaving a wide, bowl-shaped caldera.

Stage IV. After a period of quiescence new minor cones appeared on the crater floor. Some of these rise above sea level, such as Anak Krakatoa (child of Krakatoa) which appeared in 1927 and was growing as recently as 1960.

The story of the eruption and its explanation have been told at length here because of (1) the extraordinary violence of the event; (2) the interrelationship of the phenomena associated with it, such as the sea wave, the dust blanket in the atmosphere, the far-ranging sound wave, all supported by the remarkably complete way in which these unusual events were faithfully recorded; and (3) the logical fashion in which the explanation of the events of the historic eruption can be made to fit together.

This last point is the most important because it illustrates one of the leading tenets of geology; the *principle of uniformitarianism*—which freely interpreted means that processes operating today very likely operated in past geologic times in about the same way. Thus, we can use the events of the present to interpret the origin and nature of rocks and structures in the Earth's crust that were formed in ages past.

With the knowledge we have of Krakatoa's eruption, we can attack the problem of the origin of Crater Lake in Oregon.

Although Crater Lake stands at an altitude of 6,000 feet, rather than at sea level as Krakatoa does, their calderas have many similarities (figure 2).

The diameter of both craters is disproportionately large compared to the dimension of the mountain of which they are a part, and in each case most of the mountain has disappeared in the making of the caldera. It was seen to have disappeared in 1883 at Krakatoa, and its disappearance is inferred on the basis of compellingly strong evidence at Crater Lake. Arguments over the origin of Crater Lake have centered around the problem, not of the fact, of the disappearance of a volcanic mountain perhaps 12,000 feet high, to which the name Mount Mazama has been given, and containing as much as 17 cubic miles of material. Here the central issue is: was the mountain blown to bits, or was it destroyed as Krakatoa was by a combination of (1) explosion, (2) violent clearing out of the magma chamber, and (3) collapse of the unsupported volcanic edifice into the void suddenly created by the emptying of the magma chamber?

The most convincing evidence at Crater Lake, as at Krakatoa, is the fact that almost all of the immense quantity of debris surrounding the site of the vanished mountain is pumice, and since it fell on land, probably not more than 5,000 years ago, most of it has survived, and thus its volume can be estimated. According to Williams (1942):

When the culminating eruptions were over, the summit of Mount Mazama had disappeared. In its place there was a caldera between 5 and 6 miles wide and 4000 feet deep. How was it formed? Certainly not by the explosive decapitation of the volcano. Of the 17 cubic miles of solid rock that vanished, only about a tenth can be found among the ejecta. The remainder of the ejecta came from the magma chamber. The volume of the pumice fall which preceded the pumice flows amounts to approximately

Figure 2 *Crater Lake, Oregon. The caldera is 6 miles in diameter, the lake is nearly 2,000 feet deep, and the highest points on the rim are nearly 2,000 feet above the lake. Wizard Island is a small cone that erupted on the caldera floor.*

3.5 cubic miles. Only 4 per cent of this consists of old rock fragments. . . . Accordingly 11.75 cubic miles of ejecta were laid down during these short-lived eruptions. In part, it was the rapid evacuation of this material that withdrew support from beneath the summit of the volcano and thus led to profound engulfment. The collapse was probably as cataclysmic as that which produced the caldera of Krakatau in 1883.

XI

WHEN THE BRITISH SHIP *Challenger* sailed away in 1872 for its epochal three-and-a-half-year, world-circling expedition to study oceans, one of its primary tasks was to measure the ocean's depth along its route. Depth measurements at that time were tedious and primitive: A heavy lead weight was lowered at the end of a stout, long hemp line marked at equal intervals, and when the weight struck bottom the depth was noted.

It was generally expected, at that time, that beyond the sloping debris from continents, the ocean floor would be fairly flat. The *Challenger* scientists discovered, however, that the American and European sides of the Atlantic Ocean were some 2,000 fathoms (12,000 feet) deep, and that the middle part of the ocean was only about 1,000 fathoms deep. This temporarily revived interest in an ancient legend which speaks of a great continent called Atlantis that sank beneath the waves thousands of years ago.

More recent worldwide studies of the ocean bottom by oceanographic ships of many nations have revealed much information about the terrain and composition of this realm hidden beneath the waters of the globe. One of the foremost contemporary oceanographers, Francis P. Shepard, brings us up to date on methods used nowadays to explore the sediments of the ocean floors and to penetrate the rocks that lie beneath it. Authoritative, yet easily read, the selection explores a number of intriguing subjects—the ocean's age, the puzzling recent age of fossils found on the deep-ocean floor and on seamounts, the mysteries of the deep-sea trenches and the mystery of manganese nodules formed only in relatively recent times.

The Earth Beneath the Sea

Sediments of the Deep Ocean

CORING APPARATUS

Coring in the deep ocean began with the *Challenger* Expedition of 1872-1876, although cores at that time were only about one foot in length. In the present century only a few deep-ocean cores had been obtained up to the end of World War II. The German *Meteor* Expedition was responsible for a large proportion of these. Scientists on the Woods Hole Institution's *Atlantis* had begun to obtain many cores of up to about ten feet in length in various parts of the Atlantic. The *Snellius* Expedition of 1929-1930 had cored in the East Indies, which includes many deep basins, and Charles Piggot of the National Research Council had obtained cores of up to ten feet in length, using a gun to shoot the cores into the bottom. This gun, however, had too many near misses in shooting holes into the sides of vessels, so it has been abandoned.

During World War II Börje Kullenberg, who now heads the Oceanographic Insti-tute at Göteborg, Sweden, made use of the piston principle in developing an instrument that was so simple that many ocean-ographers have been wondering why they had not thought of the idea previously (figure 1). The piston corer has a trip weight that is suspended below the device. When the trip weight reaches bottom, it releases the core barrel, which falls free, while the piston that is inside the core barrel descends at a much slower rate. The brakes of the winch on the deck of the vessel are set at the time when a tension gauge gives a sudden jump, indicating that a great weight has been released from the line. (The hitting of the bottom is also indicated by a so-called ball-breaker, a device containing a glass ball that is crushed by a weight released by the impact on the bottom, resulting in an implo-sion and a loud report. The sound travels to the vessel at about 4,800 feet per second and thus is recorded on a hydrophone sus-pended over the side in time to allow set-ting the brakes on the winch.) This pre-vents coiling up of wire on the bottom.

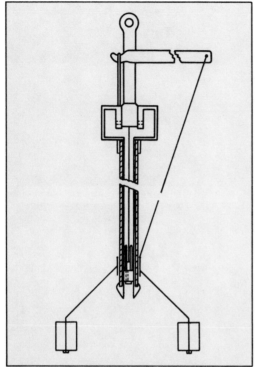

From *The Earth Beneath the Sea* by Francis P. Shepard.
© 1964 by The Johns Hopkins Press

Figure 1 *Illustration showing the principle of the Kullenberg piston corer. The trip weights are shown on the sides, and the piston in the center of the core barrel. (Gaps left to conserve space.)*

The core barrel falls free for its entire length, while the piston remains immobile. This piston action greatly reduces the effect of friction that would normally result from the core being pushed into the core barrel. This is a principle that is used by many types of soil samplers on land, but in the deep ocean the tremendous hydrostatic pressure, which is built up at the rate of one additional pound per square inch for each additional two feet of depth, acts as a differential force to drive the core barrel into the bottom. This device is one of many examples of the large contributions that the Scandinavians have made to the science of oceanography.

GLACIAL STAGES AND DEEP-SEA CORES

If you had consulted almost any geologist 25 years ago, he would probably have told you that long cores in the deep ocean would be an expensive way of finding out more about the same material you could get in a short core. The ocean must have been an ocean for a long time, so that the continuous rain of small marine animals, the dust carried out in the atmosphere and settling slowly to the great depths, and the sediment carried out from rivers or by wave action were thought to be a small but fairly constant source. Because other sediments were contributed so slowly, meteorites were said to be important in the deep-sea sediments. With these sources there seemed to be no particular reason for believing that the sediment on the sea floor should be stratified or change in character from time to time. As has so often been the case in the past, this idea, built up without much factual background, proved to be erroneous. Actually the long deep-sea cores have shown a remarkable series of alternating layers.

One of the first indications that all was not well with the old idea that the same kind of material had accumulated slowly for millions of years was brought to light by the Piggot cores shot into the ocean bottom along a line traversing the northern Atlantic Ocean. The studies of these cores showed M. N. Bramlette and W. H. Bradley of the United States Geological Survey that the deposits of the great ice age were represented in the sediments lying at depths of about one foot below the bottom. It stands to reason that during the times when the great glaciers covered northern North America, Greenland, and a considerable part of Europe great numbers of icebergs broke off from the floating margin and drifted out across the North Atlantic. These icebergs carried great quantities of stones, which were dropped as the ice melted. Since other types of deposition in the deep ocean were relatively slow, just as they are now, the stones are well represented in the deposits of these glacial stages. The Piggot cores across the North Atlantic contained layers with stones and gravel interbedded with other layers that represented the relatively warm episodes sandwiched in between the times when the earth was refrigerated.

It has been possible to connect some of the stages of the great ice age from core to core across the Piggot Atlantic traverse. Independent evidence of alternating cold and temperate climate came from a study of the character of the foraminifera in the various layers. Some of these unicellular animals that drift around near the surface of the ocean are very sensitive to temperature. Experts have learned to recognize the types that are restricted to various temperature conditions (figure 2). As the temperatures changed with the development of the ice age, the foraminifera now living in the Arctic seas moved into lower latitudes. Thus the foraminifera at a little depth below the top of the cores are of a different character from those in the surface sediments.

The most complete study of these glacial and postglacial sediment layers in the deep sea has been made by Lamont Observatory's David Ericson. His study of the foraminifera, combined with carbon-14 age determinations by W. S. Broecker and J. L. Kulp, both also of Lamont Observatory, and oxygen-18 temperature measurements by Cesare Emiliani of the University of Miami showed that the waters of the Atlantic warmed up about 11,000 years ago. (Oxygen-18 temperature measurements are taken by a method formulated by Harold Urey of the University of California, that uses the ratios between oxygen-18 and oxygen-16 isotopes obtained from shells to determine the temperature of the water in

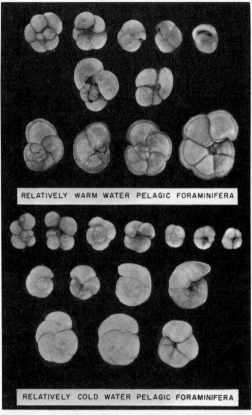

RELATIVELY WARM WATER PELAGIC FORAMINIFERA

RELATIVELY COLD WATER PELAGIC FORAMINIFERA

Courtesy F. B. Phleger, Scripps Institution of Oceanography

Figure 2 *A group of forminifera greatly magnified, used by the experts to determine whether the foraminifera were living in relatively warm or relatively cold water.*

which the shells lived.) This gives a date for the retreat of the great ice sheets that accords with other lines of evidence. The extent of the last glacial stage, which Ericson believes is about 50,000 years, is more open to controversy, others considering it much shorter.

DEEP-SEA SANDS

Geologists were not particularly disturbed by the discoveries that the great glacial period was represented by a change in sediment in the higher latitudes, but considerable surprise and some disbelief came from the later discovery that sand beds, some of them as clean as those found on the beaches and in the shallow water near shore, are well represented on portions of the deep-sea floor. The surprise became even greater when it was reported that these sand layers contain shells of foraminifera that are now living only on the bottom of shallow seas.

At first there was some thought that these deep-sea sand layers might represent great submergences, or, in other words, that the deep-sea floor had once been near the surface, where waves and currents could be expected to produce the coarse sediments. However, with the advent of the piston coring devices and the obtaining of long cores it was found that the sand layers alternate in many places with typical deep-sea deposits. The distribution of sand layers in the North Atlantic as interpreted from the Lamont coring operations has been quite adequately mapped by David Ericson (figure 3). The indications are that these

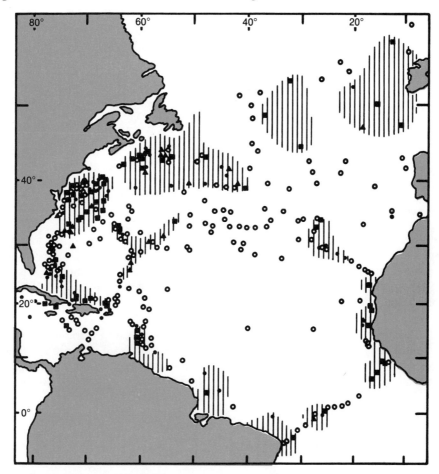

● CORES WITH GRADED SAND LAYERS   ▲ CORES WITH SILT LAYERS
■ CORES WITH SAND LAYERS NOT GRADED   ○ CORES WITHOUT SAND OR SILT LAYERS

Modified from D. B. Ericson *et al,* in *Crust of the Earth*, Geol. Soc. of Amer., 1955

Figure 3 *Location of cores with sand and silt layers (shaded areas) found on the deep floor of the Atlantic Ocean by Lamont Geological Observatory.*

sands extend out from various parts of the coast in great sea fans. They are obviously one of the manifestations of the great transporting power of turbidity currents. On the other hand, the fact that only 134 out of 550 Lamont deep-sea cores have sand layers suggests that a large part of this ocean may not be receiving the coarser turbidity-current deposits.

The other more common types of deep-sea deposits include deep-sea oozes, red clays, and terrigenous muds. The distribution of these deposits as far as it is known is indicated in figure 4.

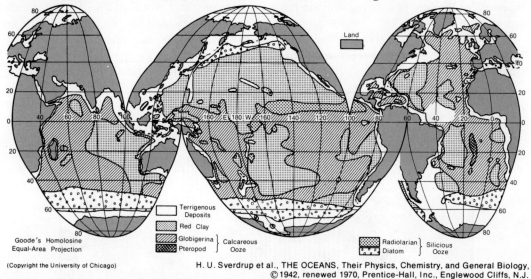

Goode's Homolosine Equal-Area Projection

(Copyright the University of Chicago)

H. U. Sverdrup et al., THE OCEANS, Their Physics, Chemistry, and General Biology, © 1942, renewed 1970, Prentice-Hall, Inc., Englewood Cliffs, N.J.

Figure 4 *The distribution of the various types of pelagic sediments.*

DEEP-SEA OOZES

The soft squashy sediments known as oozes are found in general in the shoaler portions of the deep-sea floor. The oozes consist of the minute shells or skeletons of the low types of animals and plants that drift in the surface and near-surface waters and are known as *plankton*. Of these the foraminifera are the most abundant and because the common forms are Globigerina (figure 2), the deposit in which they dominate is referred to as *globigerina ooze*. This type of ooze is found widely in the Atlantic and over rather extensive areas in the South Pacific.

DIATOM OOZE

Diatom ooze is dominated by the remains of a siliceous plant that is very common in the upper waters, at times developing almost a soupy appearance at the surface. The deposit is found in a large belt around the Antarctic and in another extensive area northeast of the Japanese Islands. In both of these areas oceanic waters of intermediate depth, which are rich in nutrients such as phosphates and nitrates, are brought up to the surface and provide the food for the plants. Large numbers of animals live on these plants, but not very much of the animal remains gets to the bottom because they are more soluble than the silica in the plants. In a few areas around the equatorial Pacific the siliceous animals known as Radiolaria are predominant in the deposits and constitute another variety of ooze.

RED CLAYS

A sediment that is predominantly clay has been found over most of the deeper portions of the ocean basins. The name *red clay* is unfortunate, since most of these deep clays are brown or bluff colored. It happened that the first samples that were obtained in the South Atlantic had a red color, so the name was established for all similar clays. The low content of calcium carbonate in the clays was at first puzzling in view of the enormous masses of free-floating organisms in the oceanic waters that must be contributing their skeletons to the ocean floor. Then it was realized that solution was sufficient in the areas because the cold carbonated waters coming from the Antarctic and moving along the deep basins remove the calcium carbonate as it sinks or dissolve it out of the slowly accumulating sediments. According to Robert Rex of Scripps Institution the clay comes largely from atmospheric dust, from fine-grained land-derived deposits that have circulated for great distances in the major ocean-current systems, to some extent from meteorites, and to a minor degree from volcanic dust.

TERRIGENOUS MUDS

The deposits that flank the continents and constitute the principal sediment of the deep-sea fans are referred to as *muds*. They differ from the red clay in having a considerable quantity of silt, and as we have learned recently, they are often interlayered with sands. These muds are predominantly land derived, probably having been transported largely by turbidity currents. The colors of the muds show a relationship to the adjacent land masses. If there are large rivers entering in the vicinity, the muds are apt to be red, representing the oxidized conditions of the river deposits. Outside dry coasts the muds are usually green. Black muds are found where stagnant basins occur along portions of the coast and where a large amount of plant and animal life is contributed. This organic debris may form future oil deposits. White muds occur on some of the steep slopes around coral islands and consist of the comminuted fragments broken from corals and other calcareous organisms of the reefs. This fine material is carried down the slopes, partly by landslides.

NONDEPOSITIONAL ZONES ON THE DEEP-SEA FLOOR

All dredgings that have been made on the seamounts or on smaller elevations of the deep-sea floor have shown that deposition of recent material, if present at all, occurs in very limited quantities and extent. This was brought home to us in 1938 when we tried to get a core at a depth of 2,000 fathoms on top of a gentle rise coming up from a surrounding sea floor of 2,400 fathoms. After working in a rough sea for hours to disentangle the last 400 fathoms of wire, we found that our core barrel had been badly smashed by hitting a rock covered with manganese. Small fragments were caught in the bent tube. One of the guyots off California that we photographed showed scattered globigerina ooze deposited in cracks of the rock surface (figure 5).

Photo courtesy of A. J. Carsola and R. S. Dietz

Figure 5 *Photograph of the rock surface of a guyot off the west coast of the United States. The white indicates globigerina ooze deposit in the cracks, and the spiked animal is an echinoid.*

Virtually all of Maurice Ewing's photographs on Atlantic seamounts show rock. Much of the seamount rock is coated with manganese, and manganese nodules are common on the ocean floor, in general indicating very slow deposition.

Perhaps more surprising is the existence of extensive zones of nondeposition on relatively flat floors of the deep Pacific. These have been established by the work of W. R. Riedel of Scripps Institution on Radiolaria obtained on the Swedish Deep Sea Expedition. Out of fifteen piston cores taken in runs from Tahiti to Hawaii and then back to the Ellice Islands (near Fiji), Riedel found that Tertiary Radiolaria occurred at or near the surface in eleven of the cores; in many localities the older Radiolaria are mixed with recent sediment. This shows that deposition in this tropical central Pacific has been amazingly slow or locally absent and that the older material is being redistributed on the ocean floor. In some localities currents of the deep-sea floor appear to be capable of removing much or all of the finer sediment that is now sifting to the bottom, only allowing some of the coarser material, such as foraminifera, to accumulate.

Ever since the *Challenger* Expedition it has been known that manganese nodules exist on the deep-ocean floor. Recent oceanographic expeditions, particularly those in the Pacific, have indicated that manganese may be so abundant on parts of the ocean floor that some day it may be possible to recover it for commercial uses by dredging, partly for the cobalt and nickel that the nodules contain. Photographs often show large clusters of these nodules protruding from the sea floor. Some of them are up to three feet in maximum diameter. The nodules have been found as thick coatings on a large proportion of the rocks dredged from seamounts both in the Atlantic and in the Pacific. It is rare that any manganese is found in cores from the ocean bottom except at the top of the cores. These nodules raise a very curious problem. Why have they formed in relatively recent times but not at more remote periods? As yet there is not even enough information to be absolutely sure that this distinction exists, let alone to explain the difference.

Another mystery not yet explained is why the fossils found to date on the deep-sea floor and on seamounts are not older than the Cretaceous. This may indicate that the oceans are not very old.

At first thought it might be supposed that a discussion of what is under the ocean bottom belongs in the realm of science fiction. Actually the information on the subject gathered in the past ten years has aroused more interest among scientists than almost any other phase of ocean study. Sound waves, used so successfully in learning about the configuration of the sea bottom, have been used also as an important means of unlocking the secrets of the earth's crust under the ocean. The results, which are still somewhat speculative, are permitting geologists and geophysicists to explain many things about the nature of deformation of the crust and to interpret on a much better basis the history of the past. So much interest has been aroused by these studies that there is now being considered the possibility of putting a drilling down for many miles into the deep-ocean bottom to check the new interpretations. This Jules Vernean scheme would have been greeted by Scientists with derision a few years ago, but now that we are launching satellites into space and drilling deep oil wells in the shallow part of the ocean floor, it does not seem like a very remote possibility to extend the drillings to the deep-ocean floor. Furthermore, the knowledge gained from an oceanic boring may have some real importance to military science.

Methods of Probing by Sound

THE SONOPROBE

Almost as soon as echo soundings began to be recorded, fathograms that indicated a reflecting surface underneath the ocean bottom were observed locally (figure 6). These records were obtained from places where very soft muds are believed to exist over firm sand or rock. In most places no sub-bottom echo can be detected on fathograms, largely because the supersonic sound (sound having more than 20,000 cycles per second, the limit audible to most people) of the echo-sounding devices is reflected mostly from the ocean bottom, and any further reflection from an underlying layer would fail to make much of an impression on the record or would become lost in the reverberation from the first echo. In very

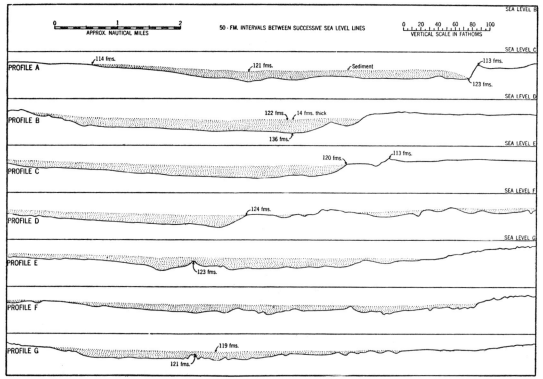

Obtained by W. H. Murray from fathograms by the U. S. Coast and Geodetic Survey

Figure 6 *Soft sediment overlying hard bottom in the Gulf of Maine.*

recent years extensive experimentation with low-frequency sound has indicated that water-saturated sediments can be penetrated by sound to depths of as much as 200 or even 300 feet, returning an echo from the underlying rock floor. This device, called a *Sonoprobe*, was developed by Magnolia Petroleum Company partly to explore the foundation material for the large platforms built by oil companies for drilling under the continental shelf. Its use has been extended to detect structures of the rock under the sediment. It operates very much like an echo-sounding device, and a record is made as the boat progresses. However, unlike fathograms, which almost anyone can interpret, the Sonoprobe records have to be monitored by an expert who must constantly regulate the device to get the proper output of sound into the water to detect the minor differences in sound from the waves passing through the sediment and reflecting from the rock beneath.

Before the Sonoprobe records could be properly interpreted, the velocity of sound through water-saturated sediments had to be determined since it is not the same as the 4,800-foot-a-second average speed of sound through ocean water. Experiments by many laboratories, notably those of A. R. Laughton of Cambridge University, John Nafe of Lamont Geological Observatory, and G. A. Shumway of the Navy Electronics Laboratory, gave results that allowed the estimation of sound velocities in unconsolidated sediments as well as in various types of rock.

ECHOES FROM EXPLOSIVE SOUND

Somewhat before the development of the Sonoprobe, sound reflections were obtained from underocean surfaces by the use of explosives that sent such powerful waves into the bottom that vibrations penetrated the top sediments and were reflected from the underlying rock surfaces (figure 7). Because of the sound intensity and reverberations, only large thicknesses of sediment can be determined in this way. The method was first employed by W. Weibull, a Swedish geophysicist from Oceanografiska Institutet in Göteborg, who accompanied Hans Pettersson of the same institution on the *Albatross* during the epoch-making Swedish voyage around the world in 1947-1948.[1] Weibull found thicknesses that varied considerably from place to place but in some

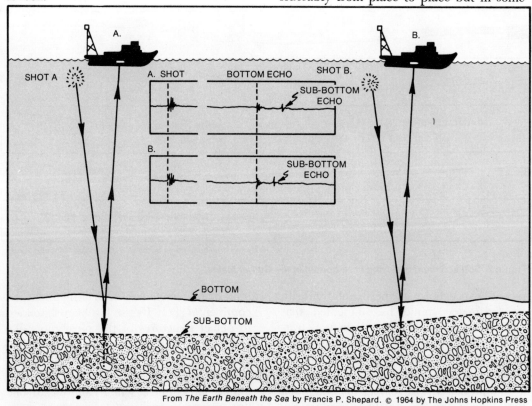

From *The Earth Beneath the Sea* by Francis P. Shepard. © 1964 by The Johns Hopkins Press

Figure 7 *Explosive used to determine the depth to the underlying rock formations. The nature of the record from which the interpretation is made is indicated in the center of the diagram.*

cases appeared to be as much as two miles. A similar method has been used to some extent by the geophysicists of Lamont Geological Observatory, Woods Hole Oceanographic Institution, and Scripps Institution of Oceanography in their explorations. Combining this method with the refraction method discussed below gives more certainty to results. The sediment thickness of the trenches of the eastern Pacific has been determined by this means.

REFRACTION WAVES FROM EXPLOSIVES

In the early twenties geologists and geophysicists began using explosive waves to determine the existence of buried rock structures in the oil fields. This work was largely responsible for changing a threatened oil famine into undreamed-of wealth for the petroleum industry. Dynamite is exploded in shallow holes, causing artificial earthquakes, and the times of arrival of waves are measured on a series of small portable seismographs set up at various distances from the shot point. Waves traveling through the earth arrive at the stations along a variety of paths and the times of arrival depend on the speed at which the waves travel through the various layers encountered en route. When the waves traveling down from the source encounter a hard layer in which vibrations travel more rapidly, they are refracted toward the horizontal and in many cases follow the contact of the hard layer, sending waves back diagonally to the surface all along the way (figure 8). Because of the high speed of travel possible along these deep layers, the waves traveling along them may reach the seismograph before the more slowly traveling waves in the surface layers. In cases where the waves traveling in the surface layer have arrived first, these surface waves may have been sufficiently deadened by the time of the second arrival that the next waves are detected in the seismograph record.

The use of these refraction waves for studying the ocean floor was begun in 1937 on Woods Hole Oceanographic Institution vessels by Maurice Ewing and his associates Allyn C. Vine of Woods Hole, J. Lamar Worzel of Lamont Geological Observatory and George P. Woollard of the University of Wisconsin. Results before World War II

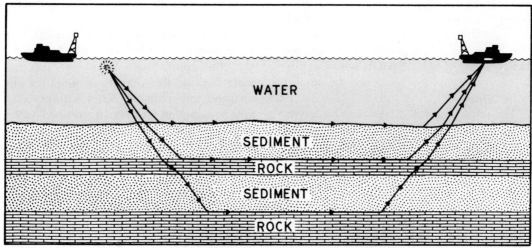

From *The Earth Beneath the Sea* by Francis P. Shepard. © 1964 by The Johns Hopkins Press

Figure 8 *Sound refraction and multiple echoes used to determine the thickness and the nature of the rock and sediment under the ocean bottom. Note that when the sound travels from rock down into underlying sediment, the ray is bent downward so that no return comes from the surface between the two.*

were spectacular but rather deceptive. Directly after the war, work began again and has centered at Lamont Geological Observatory under Maurice Ewing, at Scripps Institution under Russell W. Raitt, at Woods Hole under J. Brackett Hersey, and at Cambridge University under Sir Edward C. Bullard and Maurice N. Hill.

At first, bombs were lowered to the ocean bottom before exploding, and the vibration waves were received from a series of seismographs also placed on the bottom. These seismographs and their records were later recovered by freeing weights, which held the instrument down until a salt release dissolved in the water, dropping the weights and allowing the buoyed instrument to rise to the surface. This was a costly method and has been largely replaced since it was learned that explosives set off near the surface are almost as effective. (The sea-bottom method has been revived recently by John I. Ewing of Lamont Geological Observatory for special purposes.) With this innovation floating seismographs were strung out behind the ship, and the records were received in each of them, but it was soon found more satisfactory to set off a series of explosions from one moving vessel, with a stationary vessel receiving the sound waves on its seismographs. The distance between the vessels at points where explosives are dropped is obtained by underwater sound.

The refraction method not only has given much information on the thickness of unconsolidated sediment but also has indicated the presence of several layers underneath the sediments in which sound velocity changes abruptly.

Thickness of Deep-Ocean Sediment Cover

Many geologists have speculated on the thickness of the sediment that blankets the rock of the ocean bottom. The most painstaking attempt to arrive at a satisfactory average through use of the various methods was made by Philip Kuenen in his *Marine Geology*. Using information from various cores that showed the contact between glacial deposits and postglacial, he arrived at an average rate of accumulation of one centimeter (0.4 inch) per 1,000 years. He reasoned that a slower rate should apply to past ages because of the supposed greater elevation of the continents during the Recent period than during most of the geological ages, and because of compaction of deeply buried sediment. Applying corrections, he arrived at a figure of 1/6 centimeter per 1,000 years. Then figuring on two billion years for the age of the ocean, he estimated that the average thickness for the sediment of the ocean basins would be three kilometers (9,800 feet) or approximately two miles. Using various other methods, such as multiplying the ocean age by the estimated amount of sediment carried annually by rivers from the continents to the ocean, Kuenen obtained figures that were roughly comparable. As a result, it was anticipated that when the sediment thickness could be measured by sound waves, the results would confirm Kuenen's estimates.

We now have many sound records, but little that will confirm Kuenen. We know that the approximate thickness (approximate because the velocity of sound in unconsolidated sediment varies with porosity and compaction so that an assumed value has to be given) in the low-velocity layer down to the first good reflecting surface in many parts of the Pacific averages about 1,000 feet, and in the Atlantic it averages about 2,000 feet. The higher values in the Atlantic were expected because the rivers carry more sediment into that ocean per unit area of ocean than into the Pacific. In any case there is a great discrepancy between the Kuenen estimates and the measured values.

As yet no one has entirely explained the difference between the estimates and measurements. It is possible that the measurements have been made in areas where sediments are much thinner than the average, but this does not seem reasonable because the relatively thin sediment cover has been found in both the Atlantic and the Pacific. An alternative could be that the oceans are much younger than is generally thought to be the case. The great submergences indicated by the deep guyots, by the deep foundation of atolls, and perhaps also by the great depths of submarine canyons may imply that the ocean has been growing deeper rather rapidly since the Cretaceous period, as suggested by Roger Revelle. A rise of 5,000 feet of the sea surface during the past 70 million years (the approximate age of the Cretaceous) might mean that the ocean is less than 200 million years old (the average ocean depth being 13,000 feet). This would account for a thinner sediment cover.

An explanation that appears to offer fewer difficulties has been suggested recently by E. L. Hamilton. His suggestion is that the deeper parts of the sediment cover have been converted into rock, so that the reflection or refraction that comes at the base of the supposed sediment column is actually at the contact between the unconsolidated sediment and a consolidated sedimentary layer. If there is a sequence that consists of a consolidated layer lying between the unconsolidated sediments above and below, the existence of the underlying sediments cannot be detected by sound impulses, since the refraction of sound will be upward only where the sound passes from an unconsolidated into a consolidated layer (figure 8). Perhaps a thin layer of lava has poured out over the sediments in some places and hidden the underlying portion. If this explanation by Hamilton is correct, we would have less difficulty in interpreting past geological history than with the hypothesis of a relatively young ocean. According to most geologists the ancient formations and the fossil record seem to require an ocean throughout geological history.

Thickness of Marginal Sediments

In some places along the margins of the ocean basins there are thick masses of sediment. Off the east coast of the United States the Lamont group has found that there are two sedimentary troughs, an inner one under the continental shelf containing an estimated thickness of 17,000 feet of sediment and an outer one under the slope and adjacent ocean floor with up to 30,000 feet of sediment (figure 9). Similarly along the United States coast of the Gulf of Mexico there are 20,000 feet or more of sediment under the outer shell according to the reports of various petroleum geologists. Off California, Scripps Institution scientists have found that there is as much as 10,000 feet of sediment under the basins of the continental borderland (figure 10), but elsewhere, particularly on the ridges, rock comes right to the surface. Beyond the continental slope the sediment is more like that of the deep-ocean basins, although locally it may thicken up to about 6,000 feet.

Crustal Layers under the Ocean

THE CRUST AND MANTLE

The interpretation of refraction shooting over the ocean basins soon led to the recognition of a major discontinuity at a depth of from about three to eight miles below the bottom, averaging four miles. Below this break, sound travels at a rate of a little more than 26,000 feet a second and above the break at various slower speeds. The contact is called the *Mohorovicic discontinuity*, or the *Moho* for short. It occurs also under the continents, but here it lies at a depth of about twenty to twenty-five miles, a striking

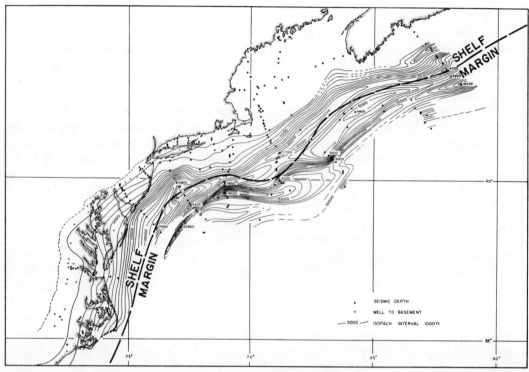

Figure 9 *Contours from C. L. Drake and M. Ewing showing the thickness in feet (isopachs) of the un-consolidated and semiconsolidated sediment off the east coast. A rise in the basement rock near the edge of the continental shelf is indicated.*

contrast with the oceanic values. Above the Moho the rock is generally referred to as the *crust* and below as the *mantle*. (There are other deeper layers, which will not be considered here because they are the same under ocean and continents.)

The discovery of the shallow Moho under the oceans has been very helpful in the explanation of the ocean depths. The rock below the Moho with its higher sound velocity is best interpreted as heavier than the rock above, since denser rocks in general have higher sound velocities. Therefore, the thicker crust under the continents with its lighter weight can balance the thinner crust under the ocean.

The Moho discontinuity is difficult to find in some places under the Mid-Atlantic Ridge. At these localities there appears to

be a gradational zone between the crust and the mantle. Sound velocities a little low for the mantle but high for the crust extend to depths that are in excess of the usual depths of the Moho under the ocean. It has been suggested that under the broad arches of the ocean floor the crust and mantle may have been mixed together by the development of molten rock along the contact.

At first it was thought that the crust under the deep oceanic trenches would be still thinner than under the rest of the ocean in order to balance these great depressions. Recently some measurements have been made, mostly by Scripps Institution geophysicists, that show the depth of the Moho under trenches of the Pacific. The Moho has been found to bend down under the

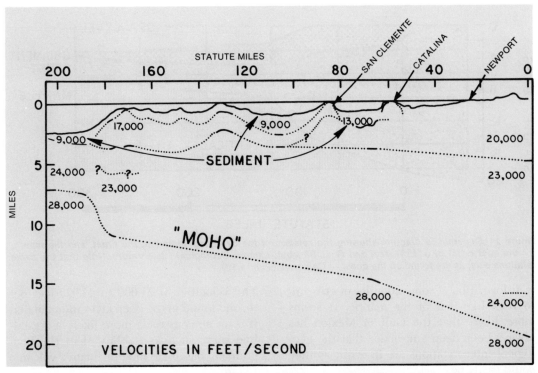

Figure 10 *Cross section by George Shor and R. W. Raitt, Scripps Institution of Oceanography, of the sea floor off Newport, southern California, showing the thickness of the sediment under the basins and the travel velocities in feet per second in the underlying rocks. The Moho disconformity is shown at the base. Note that the Moho is far deeper under the continent than under the ocean basin.*

trenches rather than up, which may imply that the trenches are being held down by some lateral force that may be possible because they are so narrow and therefore can support the weight.

The contact between the thin oceanic crust and the thick continental crust is still not entirely clear. However, there is some information that indicates that the continental shelf lies in a transition zone with the Moho dipping rather steeply toward the continent under the ocean (figure 11). The continental borderland off southern California, which has somewhat intermediate water depths between oceanic and continental, also has intermediate thickness of the crust above the Moho (figure 10). George Shor and Russell Raitt found that the Moho lies closer to the surface along the

outer borderland than it does under areas of the same depth on the inner portions of the borderland. Thus the crust thickness here, as under the trenches, is not directly related to water depth.

Another interesting result from the refraction studies has come from the investigation of relatively small basins like the Gulf of Mexico and the Arctic Ocean. It has been thought by many geologists that the Gulf of Mexico is a sunken portion of the North American continent, but the Moho in all of these relatively small basins of considerable depth is as near the bottom as under the large oceanic basins. It is difficult to believe that a continental mass with its deep Moho could be transformed into an ocean basin with its shallow Moho. Such a change would have to include a

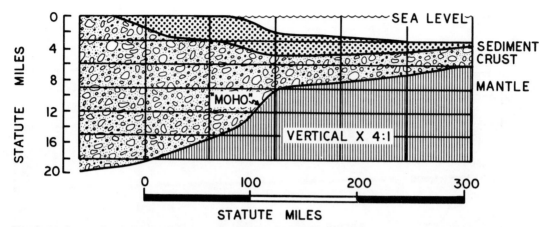

Figure 11 *Generalized diagram showing the relation of the overlying sediment, the crust, and the mantle for the east coast by J. L. Worzel and G. L. Shurbet, Lamont Geological Observatory. Note that the same relations exist as are found off the coast of California (Figure 10).*

transformation of some 20 miles of crust into rock like that of the mantle. It seems more likely that the Gulf of Mexico has always been deep and hence that the geological interpretations are in error, as they could easily be.

ITERMEDIATE CRUSTAL LAYERS

In the early interpretations of refraction shooting over the ocean floor only one crustal layer was recognized under the sediment cover. Later, however, the extensive work by Russell Raitt and his colleagues in the Pacific showed that there was definitely another layer. This same layer has since been discovered in the Atlantic by various investigators. As it now stands there is a downward sequence as follows: the sediment layer with an average velocity of 7,000 feet per second, the first rock layer with an average velocity of 16,000 feet per second, and the deep crustal layer with an average velocity of 22,000 feet per second. The upper rock layer could be either sedimentary rock, such as limestone, or lava. Around volcanic islands some of the velocities are as low as 16,000 feet per second, and these are almost certainly lavas with many gas cavities or the rocks are highly fractured.

The velocities of 21,000 to 23,000 feet per second found in the deep layer indicate that it is an igneous rock, more likely a crystalline rock, such as gabbro, than the fine-grained basalt found in many volcanic islands.

Gravity Interpretations for the Ocean Basins

Another method of diagnosing the nature of the rock under the oceans is by measuring the pull of gravity. This has been accomplished by timing the swing of a pendulum in a submerged submarine, where there is a minimum of wave disturbance. At any given spot the swing of a pendulum has a constant period. The greater the pull of gravity, the faster the pendulum will swing. It is necessary, however, to get a very accurate timing of the period, since differences are only a few parts in a million. In addition, the topography must be taken into account. The higher the elevation at which the pendulum is swung, the farther the station lies from the center of mass and hence the slower the swing. Thus corrections have to be made for topography even though all ocean measurements are made at almost exactly the same height. However, in oceanic gravity measurements a correction has to be made for depth of water, since water is lighter than rock and will therefore not have as much gravitative pull. Once these and some other corrections have been made, the reading of gravity gives an idea of the relative heaviness of material underlying the area where the measurement has been made.

Gravity studies in the ocean have shown that in all probability the oceanic crust as a whole is balanced against the continents just as a heavy piece of wood floating in a pail of water is balanced against a light piece of wood, the former rising less above the water surface. The continents rise above the ocean-bottom level because they are underlain by lighter material. The gravitative studies are essentially in agreement with those of explosive waves and earthquake vibrations, since in general the heavier rocks have also higher speeds of wave travel. The gravity measurements are used to help determine the thickness of crustal layers, work in which Vening Meinesz of the Netherlands and in recent years J. Lamar Worzel of Lamont Geological Observatory have been leaders.

One of the interesting results of gravity measurements has been the finding of areas with decidedly deficient gravity wherever the deep-sea trenches have been investigated. This has led to the speculation that the trenches may be held down by lateral pressure, due perhaps to convection currents that move the crust and produce mountain ranges in other places. A difference of opinion has developed regarding the interpretation of the gravity anomalies and the crust under the trenches. The Lamont group has maintained on the basis of gravity measurements that the crust is very thin under the trenches, but as indicated previously the seismic shooting by Scripps Institution scientists indicates that the crust is relatively thick and the Moho bends down under the trenches. No doubt continued work will soon solve this difference of opinion. Interpretations are still subject to much uncertainty.

References

[1]Hans Petterson, *Westward Ho with the Albatross* (New York: E. P. Dutton & Co., 1953).

XII

THE OCEAN HAS SPARKED man's curiosity since the first primitive human being stood on the shores of an early sea, looked off to the horizon of this great pulsating body of water and wondered where the waves came from. Men that followed him have accumulated a great storehouse of knowledge of the sea, but not as much as they have learned about the lands on which they farm or build their cities.

Oceanography is a burgeoning, relatively new science. It includes a multitude of overlapping and interrelated things. It is not a distinct discipline, but rather a field of geology in which many disciplines find relevance. William S. von Arx, a noted oceanographer, introduces this branch of geology in the next brief selection.

Oceanography

Reprinted by permission of the publisher from William S. von Arx, *An Introduction to Physical Oceanography* (Reading, Mass.: Addison-Wesley Publishing Company, Inc., 1962), pp. 1-2.

OCEANOGRAPHY, an assemblage of many sciences oriented toward a study of the earth's oceans, is principally concerned with various aspects of sea water: its motions and chemical constituents, its physical properties and behavior, its relationships to the solid earth, the atmosphere, and to living organisms of all kinds, its economic and technical potentialities, its role as a part of the earth's outer covering. Where sea water wets the solid crust, oceanography enters the domain of geology. Where it reflects sunlight, is distilled into the atmosphere or exerts a drag on the winds, oceanography is joined with meteorology. Where marine forms of life exist or land forms migrate by way of the sea, oceanography merges with biology. And where man must combat or find uses for the sea or sea water itself, oceanography is allied with engineering and technology. Oceanography is concerned with the sea as a major part of the human environment. It is a relatively unspecialized field, and a large number of disciplines find application within its boundaries.

In the traditional view oceanography is subdivided into three main branches: physical oceanography, chemical oceanography, and biological oceanography. But this classical subdivision is restrictive. Today it is equally appropriate to include marine meteorology, submarine geology and geophysics, and certain branches of engineering as fundamental parts of the science.

Physical oceanography involves two major activities: (1) a direct observational study of the oceans and the preparation of synoptic charts of oceanic properties, and (2) a theoretical study of the physical processes which might be expected to lead to the observed behavior of the oceans. The first is a branch of physical geography and the second is a branch of theoretical physics. Neither can stand without chemical and biological information as a part of the description of the oceans and as a cross-check on the validity of physical reasoning.

The chemist's role in the study of the oceans is nearly central, being as indispensable to physical as it is to biological studies. Through chemical analysis we have learned that the composition of the salt dissolved in sea water is, in a broad way, nearly the same regardless of its total concentration, which suggests that the whole world ocean is well mixed, and we infer that this mixture must be sustained by various classes of currents. Chemistry also provides a method for determining the density of sea water. From a knowledge of sea-water density as a function of depth, it has become possible to compute the field of relative motion in the sea that contributes to the mixing process.

Near shore the "constancy of composition" of sea water cannot be assumed to hold even approximately. Dissolved inorganic and organic materials from rivers, industrial wastes, and ground water constitute an important environmental influence on the productivity of organisms in the sea. These problems make the work of the chemist nearly indistinguishable from that of the biologist.

Biologists often work in association with both chemists and physicists to determine the relations between organisms and their environment. Part of the biologist's problem is to determine the organic and inorganic intake of organisms, the cycles by which these materials are returned to supply future generations, and the paths these materials take through the food cycle of the sea. Lately radiochemical evidence has been used to trace substances through the food chain as well as to study the characteristics of predation and the diseases of organisms. When the source of radioactive material is localized in space and time, some inferences can be drawn concerning the migrations of the larger pelagic forms of life.

These interrelated investigations have bearing on the fishing industry, which is at present the most important economic contribution of the oceans. Economic oceanography, however, leads beyond fishery resources to consideration of waste-disposal problems, the recovery of metals and salts from the sea, the extraction of power from waves and tides, a study of the motion of ships in a seaway and of the management of ships so as to take advantage of favorable currents and weather, the conversion of sea water to potable water, and the construction of well-drilling platforms which will withstand the onslaught of waves and the erosion of currents. The engineering difficulties attending the construction of offshore platforms have received recent public notice, but in the background there is the quiet triumph of the submarine telegraph companies which have maintained lines on the sea bed for more than a century. This achievement was based on a scientific study of the sea undertaken to satisfy an economic need. Such motivation has been mainly responsible for progress in the science from the earliest times.

XIII

As MAN TRAVELS AWAY from earth into space, he is impressed by the realization that this is a water planet. The oceans glittering in the sun make the earth appear to be a sparkling ball against the darkness of space. Viewing the earth from a distance, as our astronauts do, drives home another fact we often forget: The earth is an astronomical body. The interplay of sunlight on the earth, the radiation of earth's heat into space, rotation and gravitation all work to maintain the earth we know.

William S. von Arx next discusses some of the hypotheses and evidence concerning the geological and astronomical phenomena that have formed the earth and its oceans.

On Geological and Astronomical Backgrounds

Reprinted by permission of the publisher from William S. von Arx, *An Introduction to Physical Oceanography* (Reading, Mass.: Addison-Wesley Publishing Company, Inc., 1962), pp. 19-38.

ACCORDING to a casual definition, the earth can be regarded as being composed of three materials, rock, water, and air, arranged in three layers—the lithosphere, hydrosphere, and atmosphere. The earth is also an astronomical body, and lacking this condition very few of the present concerns of geologists, oceanographers, and meteorologists would remain. The effects of the nonuniform distribution of sunlight over the earth and the equally energetic but more uniform radiation of earth heat into space, acting with rotational and gravitational forces, produce a complex of interdependent fluid phenomena which characterize the world as we know it. In this chapter we will review some of the facts and hypotheses concerning the geological and astronomical setting of the world ocean that bear upon its properties and phenomena.

The Geometry of the Oceans

The oceans represent only 1/790 of the volume of the earth but are conspicuous because they are so extraordinarily thin in comparison with their horizontal dimensions. Indeed, on a globe they are well represented by the thickness of varnish or at most by the thickness of the paper on which a map is printed, since they average only 1/1680 of the earth's radius in depth. Oceanographers are accustomed to think of the ocean in terms of diagrams which are strongly exaggerated in the vertical dimension. This habit can lead to misconceptions. But there is no simple alternative, for sections of oceans drawn to the natural scale and printed in a book the width of this one might extend from margin to margin but from top to bottom be hardly more than a thin line. Under most circumstances a drawing to natural scale could be fitted on the edge of a page.

In spite of the almost vanishing thickness of the ocean layer compared with its width, the average depth of the oceans is approximately 4 km. According to recent estimates, the total area of the globe is 510,100,934 km², of which the land area is 148,847,000 km² (29%), while that of the sea is 361,254,000 km² or about 71% of the whole. The volume of sea water on the earth is close to 1,369,000,000 km³ and comprises more than 98% of the hydrosphere.

The *world ocean* is composed of three branches extending northward from a circumpolar ring around the Antarctic continent (figure 1). The Atlantic branch is the longest, stretching from the Antarctic

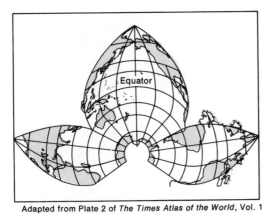

Adapted from Plate 2 of *The Times Atlas of the World*, Vol. 1

Figure 1 *The world ocean in Bartholomew's petal projection.*

Ocean to the Arctic Sea. The Pacific branch reaches northward to the Bering Strait and, by the shallowness of this passage, is effectively cut off from the Arctic basin. In spite of this abbreviation, the Pacific Ocean is so wide it covers nearly one-third of the globe. The Indian Ocean branch is the shortest, covering roughly one-seventh of the earth's surface. This seventh, however, lies mainly in the tropics and is adjacent to the largest land mass on the earth, so that the continentality of the land exerts a marked influence on its circulation.

The Atlantic Ocean system, covering one-fifth of the earth, is in effect a broad channel whose properties are subject to the gradual variation of climate with latitude from south to north. The floor of the Atlan-

tic arm is divided by an extensive mid-ocean ridge (figure 2). The North Atlantic, almost at the end of this arm, is a kind of cul-de-sac, but it is the area that has been studied most intensively. This may be unfortunate, because the generalizations drawn from studies of the North Atlantic waters may not be wholly valid for other ocean situations.

As the hub of the world ocean, the Antarctic circumpolar sea exerts an influence on each of the three arms. The melting ice of Antarctica and excess of precipitation over evaporation in summer tend to freshen the Antarctic coastal waters, but at the same time the climate is so frigid that these waters are still dense enough to sink and produce a layer of cold, relatively fresh water overlying the bottom of most ocean areas in the Southern Hemisphere. In winter the production of new sea ice increases the water density even more by slightly enriching its salt content. Through these effects on its density and its sheer abundance, Antarctic cirumpolar water extends its influence even into parts of the world ocean in the Northern Hemisphere.

The bergs characteristically calved from the shelf ice in the Weddell and Ross Seas are tabular blocks sometimes tens of miles long, several miles wide, and hundreds of feet thick. These are different from the splintered bergs (figure 3), usually encountered in the Northern Hemisphere, which are calved from distributary glaciers connected with the Greenland icecap. The few tabular bergs that exist in the Arctic Sea (figure 4), the "ice islands," appear to be derived from piedmont glaciers and are

Norfolk, Virginia

Shelf   Continental   Bermuda Is.

Slope

Rise

Mid Atlantic Ridge

Rio de Oro
North Africa

Adapted from *The Floors of the Oceans*, (Geological Society of America, New York, 1959).

Figure 2 *A topographic profile across the North Atlantic basin. Vertical scale exaggerated.*

Official U. S. Coast Guard Photograph

Figure 3 *A Coast Guard icebreaker skirts a splintered berg 269 feet long in Baffin Bay, Greenland.*

Official U. S. Coast Guard Photograph

Figure 4 *The ship (lower right in photo) is dwarfed by a tabular berg three quarters of a mile long.*

therefore very small in comparison with the Antarctic variety, although large enough to support geophysical observatories for a period of years.

Peripheral to the world ocean are the *marginal seas*. These bodies of water are characteristically adjacent to continents and enclosed by island arcs. They vary widely in depth, shape, and size. Most of them are found on the east coast of Asia—the South China Sea, East China Sea, Sea of Japan, Sea of Okhotsk, and the Bering Sea—but the Kara and Barents Seas on the north of Asia, the Arabian and Andaman Seas on the south of Asia, and the Caribbean Sea on the southeast coast of North America also qualify.

These features have close relatives in the seas less intimately associated with continents but also delineated by island chains, namely, the Coral Sea, Java Sea, Celebes Sea, and Bismark Sea of the southwest Pacific Archipelago. The Tasman Sea east of Australia and the Scotia and Weddell Seas adjacent to the Antarctic continent are varieties of marginal seas which press the definition by being exceptionally well connected with the world ocean.

The *mediterranean seas* of the earth seem epicontinental but are of nearly oceanic depth and connected to the world ocean by shallow straits. The prototype for these is the European Mediterranean, but the Arctic Ocean and the Gulf of Mexico can also be classed as mediterranean seas.

Among the least of the arms of the ocean are the inland seas. Some of these are quite salt if they are fed by rivers and drained mainly by evaporation. In time some reach complete dryness, leaving deposits of evaporite in their basins.

Others become more and more salt and may eventually become anaerobic at depth if their connection with the ocean is blocked by a shallow sill. These many, and often ephemeral, features of the hydrosphere are more closely akin to lakes than to oceans.

The Age of the Oceans

The age of the world ocean has not been established, but some limits can be stated. The ocean cannot be older than the earth itself. Measurements of uranium-lead ratios in samples from the pre-Cambrian rocks of Canada and South Africa show that the solid parts of the earth may be as old as 2800 million years. The primordial earth may be twice that old, or even more, and still not be older than the universe, whose age is variously estimated at between 5 and 10 billion years. It remains even now to learn whether or not the primordial crust was covered by ocean water to anything like the present extent.

One of the first methods used to determine the age of the ocean was to divide the total salt content of the world ocean by the annual increment of salt discharged into the sea by rivers. This procedure was suggested by Edmund Halley in 1715 but not implemented until 1899 when Joly made the first estimate using data on the abundance of sea salt obtained by the *Challenger* expedition. According to F. W. Clarke's summary of *The Data of Geochemistry*, the result of several such computations of the salt age is somewhat less than 100 million years, depending upon the figures used. This period of existence is clearly too brief, because marine organisms very like present-day species have been found in early Cambrian and some late pre-Cambrian rocks of an age which, measured by radioactive decay methods, turns out to be in the order of 500 million years. Recent studies by Woodcock and others have shown that the salt in rivers can be quantitatively accounted for in terms of "cyclic sea salts" derived from spray and droplets formed by bubbles bursting on the sea surface. Because of their small size these droplets evaporate rapidly into the lower air, and the tiny crystals of salt remaining are carried aloft by the winds to be distributed more or less uniformly over the earth. Most of these minute salt particles serve as nuclei for the condensation of rain and eventually find their way back to the ocean either directly or by way of the watersheds and rivers of the world.

It is generally assumed that the oceans are at least as old as marine fossils, and that they have been salt as far back as upper Silurian time when very thick salt beds were deposited. (Thus far the age of the oceans has also eluded measurement by radioactive decay methods. Carbon-14 methods have been used to show the time elapsed since a parcel of water was last exposed to the air. In the mid-depths of the North Atlantic the values seem to center around 400 years.)

The Origins of Sea Water

Closely associated with the age of the world ocean is the question of the origin of such a vast quantity of water (about 1 billion km³) and of the salt (about 3%) that it contains. Early speculations were concerned with a deluge. At the beginning of the nineteenth century when Hutton (1785) and Playfair (1802) proposed the uniformitarian doctrine, such ideas as the cataclysmic appearance of the lands and sea were in general currency, partly in response to Biblical legend. But it can be shown that at present temperatures the atmosphere, fully saturated, can hold no more than some 13,000 km³ of water at any one time. As water vapor over a molten earth at perhaps 1200°C, only 16% of the present ocean volume would have remained in gaseous equilibrium, and the outer part of this atmosphere would have been subjected to photochemical dissociation. Moreover, both the molecular and the dissociated water would have been far enough from the earth for the velocity of escape to be exceeded by

a large fraction of the ions and molecules. Therefore it seems probable that the water of the oceans may have been supplied in other ways, perhaps by being released slowly from within the earth and at temperatures lower than that of molten rock.

Studies of volcanic gases show that both the halogens and the water of the oceans might have been exsolved from the rocks forming the earth's crust. Goranson found that between 3 and 8% water will dissolve in molten rocks having a composition range from basalt to granite under temperatures and hydrostatic pressures approaching those supposed to exist in volcanic pipes and intrusive magmas within the crust of the earth. Studies of the emission of volcanoes by Fenner (1926) and Zies (1929) in the Katmai region of Alaska show that in addition to water, quantities of halogens, especially chlorides and fluorides, are liberated with sulphurous substances from active volcanoes.

The history of the earth has included a succession of widespread outbreaks of volcanic activity. It is possible that the present abundance of chloride ion in the ocean may have been supplied by volcanic emission, provided that the halogens in modern volcanic gases have not been derived from oceanic infiltration (figure 5). (Most modern volcanoes are fairly close to the edges of the continents or have formed islands in the sea.) If the halogens were supplied to the sea by volcanoes, it seems probable that sodium and other metallic ions have a different origin because they occur in other than the proportions required for nonexotic chemical combination. It has been calculated that the sodium, magnesium, and other metallic constituents of sea water can be accounted for by the chemical weathering of igneous rocks accompanying rainfall and runoff in the presence of carbonic acid derived from atmospheric carbon dioxide.

In view of the miscibility of water in

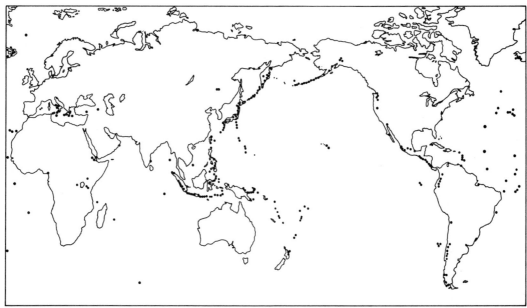

Figure 5 *Locations of the world's active volcanoes.*

molten rock under pressure and the fact that this water exsolves as the rock material crystallizes, it is of interest to compute the volume of water that could be derived from the earth's crust and compare this result with the volume of water in the oceans. The land of the earth covers an area of some 150 million km². The continental crust averages 33 km in thickness. Therefore the volume of continental crust amounts to about 6 billion km³. The crust under the oceans is much thinner, about 5 km, but more extensive, covering an area of some 360 million km². Therefore the volume of crustal rock in the ocean floor is about 2 billion km³. The total volume of the earth's crust is about 8 billion km³. If this rock volume yielded 5% free water upon crystallization, we would expect the ocean volume to be about ½ billion km³. But the ocean volume exceeds 1 billion km³, and this result requires either a larger yield of water from the crust than we have assumed or a contribution of water from additional sources such as the upper part of the mantle beneath the crust.

Stability of the Ocean Basins

The continental blocks of the earth's crust are generally composed of material of lesser density than that of the crust underlying the oceans. Crystal aggregates of the land are rich in aluminum silicates, whereas the denser rocks underlying the ocean tend to contain iron and magnesium in preference to aluminum. The fact that the land is less dense and stands higher than the sea bed, and that the anomalies of the gravitational field of the earth over the land and sea are both relatively small, suggests that the crust of the earth is floating on a still denser mantle.

An increase of density with depth is also required to provide the earth with its proper moment of rotational inertia.

The dissipation of energy in shallow seismic waves rises with the first power of their frequency, which is the case for jointed solids. From this it appears that the outer 1000 km or so of the earth may be jointed but will sustain uncompensated loads up to a point and then fail by elastic or plastic deformation only sufficiently to gain from buoyancy what it lacks in its own strength.

The level at which the crust can be distinguished from the mantle is usually related to the depth of a sharp discontinuity in the velocity of propagation of earthquake waves which has been shown to exist under both the continental and oceanic crustal rocks. This discontinuity was discovered in central European seismograms by A. Mohorovičić in 1909 and independently by several others from observations made elsewhere on the earth. Seismic data taken to establish the depth of the Mohorovičić discontinuity show that the crustal rocks of continents have an average thickness of about 33 km, whereas the crust under the oceans is relatively thin, averaging about 5 km (figure 6). This, in conjunction with the difference in density of continental and oceanic crustal rock, suggests that they

represent different end products of the chemical and physical processes that produced the earth's crust. Moreover, it is observed that the gravitational field of the earth is not markedly different from that which would be expected for a rotating spheroid in hydrostatic equilibrium. The continents rise above the general level of the crust because they extend their bulk deeply enough into the mantle for the buoyant forces in the displaced volume of mantle rock to support their excessive weight in comparison with that of the oceanic crust.

Because of the major chemical and physical reorganization that would be involved in changing the crustal thickness and composition from an oceanic to a continental configuration, it seems improbable that extensive transformations of this type have occurred.

Accumulation of material in sedimentary basins or geosynclines, followed by compression and folding to produce mountains, can increase the area of continental crust and presumably decrease the area allotted

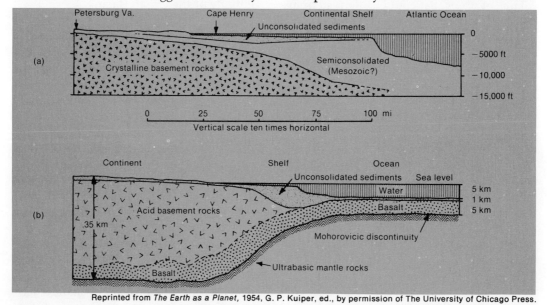

Reprinted from *The Earth as a Planet*, 1954, G. P. Kuiper, ed., by permission of The University of Chicago Press.

Figure 6 *(a) Section across the Atlantic coastal plain, as measured by Ewing. (b) Generalized section across a stable continental margin.*

to the oceans. To thin the continental crust and restore it to an oceanic thickness and composition requires the invocation of sufficient heat from the mantle to melt away the continental block from below. There is geologic evidence to support the first possibility, but at present there is understandably little to suggest that the second is important. From this we are led to presume that although mountain building has thickened the crust in some areas, such thickening is not easily restored to the oceanic configuration even under the influence of prolonged erosion.

It is thought that as erosion removes the upper surface of a continental block, a continental mass rises step by step, under its own buoyancy in the heavier rocks of the mantle, to replace from below a large fraction of the volume of material removed layer by layer from the surface. Since the rate of subaerial erosion decreases with lessening elevations and ceases altogether when the block is planed off at sea level, it would take an extraordinarily long time, even in the geological sense, for erosion to obliter-

ate any major positive feature on the earth unless sea level were steadily lowered or submarine slumping were commonplace.

The process of crustal equilibration may, at times, become "stuck" by the strength of the crust acting to retard the final stages of isostatic recovery. The fact that there are gravity anomalies also suggests that the earth's crust has strength of its own. Jeffreys estimates this strength to be sufficient to support differential pressures of as much as 100 bars.

Geological studies of the extent of continental glaciation made it seem probable that during the Pleistocene period, when large volumes of water were locked up as ice on the land surface, storm waves beat on what are now deeply submerged shelf regions of the continental margins. In 1936 R. A. Daly suggested that these soft sediments under the pounding of storm waves would produce great quantities of suspended matter which, as a highly dilute mud, would be more dense than sea water and tend to flow down the continental slopes (figure 7), eroding canyons on their way

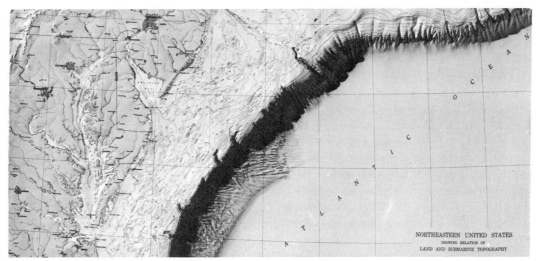

Courtesy A. J. Nystrom & Co.

Figure 7 *A relief map based on a topographic survey made by Veatch and Smith of the continental shelf and abyssal slope off New England.*

into the abyss. In 1937 Ph. H. Kuenen developed these ideas experimentally, giving the name *turbidity current* to the muddy slurries and gravity-driven suspension flows so derived. Spectacular evidence of a contemporary suspension flow (figure 8) was found by Heezen and Ewing (1952) who reasoned, in connection with an earthquake in the Grand Banks region, that a mass of slope material may have slumped onto the Telegraph Plateau southeast of Newfoundland to account for the successive rupture of five transatlantic telegraph cables in the course of a few hours. The positions of these cables were known, as well as the time at which each one parted. This permitted computation of the speed of flow, which turned out to be on the order of 50 knots. The erosive power of suspension flows of clay and silt-laden water is now considered, in addition to rafting by melting icebergs, to be a cause of the anomalous appearance of sand and other rather coarse materials in the deep parts of the ocean basins. Thus it is beginning to appear that glacial conditions are not necessary to the existence of suspension flows and that if submarine slumping is commonplace it may contribute, perhaps significantly, to the erosion of continents below sea level.

Fluctuations of Sea Level

Within the period of recorded history, sea level has been remarkably stable. At present it is only in areas where the continental ice sheet of Pleistocene time has melted and removed its weight from the land that sea level shows a rapid and persistent local change. In the northern Baltic, the Gulf of Bothnia, the deglaciated land is rising at a rate of approximately one meter per century. Similarly the basins of the Great Lakes of North America are observed to be tilting toward the south as a consequence of the elastic and plastic recoil of the continent relieved some 12,000 years

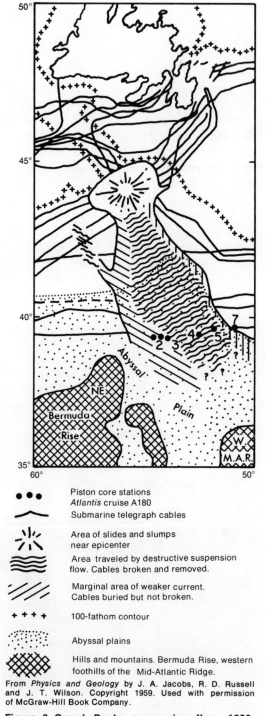

● ● ●   Piston core stations *Atlantis* cruise A180

〜   Submarine telegraph cables

Area of slides and slumps near epicenter

Area traveled by destructive suspension flow. Cables broken and removed.

Marginal area of weaker current. Cables buried but not broken.

+ + + +   100-fathom contour

Abyssal plains

Hills and mountains. Bermuda Rise, western foothills of the Mid-Atlantic Ridge.

From *Physics and Geology* by J. A. Jacobs, R. D. Russell and J. T. Wilson. Copyright 1959. Used with permission of McGraw-Hill Book Company.

Figure 8 Grand Banks suspension flow, 1929.

ago of the massive load of the continental ice sheet. In most other parts of the world the average sea level is probably rising slowly because of general melting of land-born ice.

If estimates of the thickness of the ice during the Pleistocene glaciation are reliable, it seems possible that sea level was perhaps 100 meters below the present level in mid-Wisconsin time. This is sufficient to expose most of the present continental shelves. If the continuing amelioration of climate causes the polar galciers in Greenland and Antarctica to melt completely, sea level may be expected to rise as much as several tens of meters above its present stand.

In the longer view of time, there is evidence of extensive flooding of the continents during the Paleozoic, Mesozoic, and Cenozoic eras. These events took place prior to the spasm of mountain building taken to mark the close of each of these major divisions of geologic time. There is no evidence to indicate the kind of mechanisms that caused the level of the world ocean to change. A variation of the total volume of sea water could be imagined but is hard to accept. A general flooding could result from the coordinated subsidence of the several continental blocks. But it is more plausible to imagine that flooding was caused by a buckling of some part of the sea floor. This possibility requires that the stratographic sequence of marine deposits should tend to follow a similar pattern over the entire land area of the earth. Such is only very roughtly the case.

At the present time, the average height of land above sea level is 840 meters, and the average depth of the ocean is 3790 meters. The maximum height of land above sea level is 8840 meters, and the greatest depth in the ocean may exceed 10,860 meters. A sounding of 5940 fathoms (10,860) meters) was made in the Marianas trench at lati-

tude 11°20′N, longitude 142°16′E by R. R. S. *Challenger* in 1951. The extremes of relief amount to about 1/324 of the earth's radius, which is only a little less than the earth's rotational ellipticity, 1/297.

In general, the greatest depths of the ocean are associated with the trenches bordering island arcs. These trenches support negative gravity anomalies, which suggests either that light roots extend deep into the mantle or that the trenches are tension cracks where crustal rock substance is simply absent.

Rigidity of the Earth

Those studying the strength and structure of the earth commonly consider that rocks have viscous rather than rigidly solid properties. This apparently strange point of view arises from the fact that rock substance exposed to deforming forces for different lengths of time will behave in ways which through ordinary experience we associate with materials such as wax, tar, or even "silly putty." That is, rock substance will transmit vibration by elastic deformation; sustain substantial temporary loads but break under moderate tension; flow a little in response to prolonged pressure differences; and, under sufficient confining pressure and high enough temperature, move like a liquid without actually melting.

It is often assumed that at depth in the earth the temperature as well as the confining pressure is sufficiently high to permit rock materials to change their properties enough to flow or possibly even to develop cells in which convective overturning is sustained by the evolution of radiogenic heat in the mantle. The crustal rocks floating on top of such convective cells would be exposed to horizontal shearing stresses. There is a question of quantitative sufficiency involved, but many geologic theories of mountain building and continental migration invoke convective motion in the earth's mantle as the prime mover.

Following this line of thought, it is not inconceivable that the continents have drifted over the earth from time to time in the geologic past, thereby changing the shapes but not necessarily the total areas of the oceans (figure 9).

The quasi-fluid behavior of the earth's interior would lead one to expect the settling of dense materials so as to produce a stable layering of the substances within the earth. This possibility is shown to have a basis in fact through the simple but very exacting Cavendish experiments. From these the total mass of the earth has been found to be 5.976×10^{27} gm. From the known volume of the earth it follows that

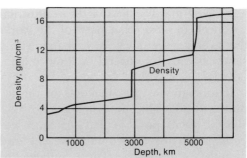

Reprinted from *The Earth as a Planet*, 1954, G. P. Kuiper, ed., by permission of The University of Chicago

Figure 10 *Density of the earth as a function of depth.*

its mean density is 5.522 gm/cm³, while that of surface rocks is near 2.7 gm/cm³.

These results require an increase of density toward the center of the earth (figure 10) but give no information as to the gradient of increase. The probable distribution of density can be estimated by reconciling the required total mass with a number of other facts and conditions. For instance, the rotational inertia of the hypothetical mass distribution must agree with that obtained from astronomical measurements of the rate of equinoxial precession and the secular rate of change of the earth's rate of rotation. The ratio of the volume elasticity and density of the material must provide seismic velocities that agree with the observed values and change at the proper levels to account for strong seismic reflections. Since there is, as yet, no direct evidence of the internal composition of the earth, and the effects of high pressure and temperature are known only for surface materials, it is only natural that a variety of earth models have been proposed. Although there is no agreement in detail, the main features of such models are alike in resembling the structure outlined in table 1.

The important fact concerning us here is that the earth seems to behave as a viscous fluid or plastic solid under sustained stress but as an elastic solid when the stress

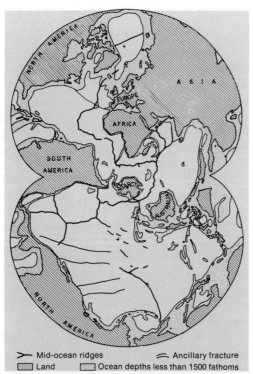

> — Mid-ocean ridges   ⌒ Ancillary fracture
▨ Land   ▢ Ocean depths less than 1500 fathoms

From *Physics and Geology* by J. A. Jacobs, R. D. Russell and J. T. Wilson. Copyright 1959. Used with permission of McGraw-Hill Book Company.

Figure 9 *The principal fracture systems and central mountain chains of oceanic crust.*

TABLE 1[°]

	Thickness, km	Volume, × 10^{27} cm³	Mean density, gm/cm³	Mass, × 10^{27} gm	Mass, %
Atmosphere	. . . .	. . . .	. . . .	0.000006	0.0001
Hydrosphere	3.80	0.00137	1.025	0.00140	0.024
Crust (land)	33.	0.0049	2.7	0.013	0.23
Crust (sea)	5.	0.0018	3.0	0.005	0.08
Mantle	2888.	0.902	4.5	4.059	68.1
Core	3471. (equivalent)	0.175	10.7	1.876	31.5
Whole earth	6371.	1.083	5.52	5.976	99.95

[°] Adapted from B. Mason, 1954, p. 261, *The Earth as a Planet*, G. P. Kuiper, editor, Chicago: University of Chicago Press.

is, geologically speaking, instantaneous. Most of the short-lived stresses on the earth are periodic or quasi-periodic. Frequencies ranging from cycles per day or a week to a full year exist in the tide-producing forces, in the diurnal and longer-period variations in the surface pressure of the atmosphere, and in the weight of water substance precipitated on the crust. To all these forces the earth seems to respond elastically. It is, in part, the difference between the elastic inphase response of the solid earth (some 30 cm) and the lagging fluid response of the oceans that permits the rise and fall of the astronomical tides. But under the sustained centrifugal force of rotation, the solid earth and its fluids respond alike and acquire an ellipsoidal figure.

Figure of the Earth

If the earth were a nonrotating homogeneous or concentrically layered sphere, the change in the direction of a plumb line would be uniform for every unit of distance traversed over the earth's surface. This was the assumption made by Eratosthenes when he measured the circumference of the earth from observations of the difference in the slope of the sun's noon rays at two points in different latitudes. But the fact

is, of course, that plumb-line verticals taken all over the earth's surface do not converge at a point. The earth has a more nearly ellipsoidal shape produced by the centrifugal reaction to rotation of every part of its substance.

According to the Newtonian concept of gravitation, each particle of the earth is attracted to every other particle with a force that varies directly as the product of the two masses and inversely as the square of the distance between them. A free particle at rest in some latitude on the rotating earth is on the whole attracted toward a point near the earth's geometrical center by Newtonian gravitation and at the same time urged away from the earth's axis by the centrifugal force of rotation. The composition of the centrifugal force of rotation with the force of gravitation, would tend to produce a component of force directed toward the equator were it not that the ellipsoidal figure of the earth provides a "downhill" component of the force of gravitational attraction away from the equator which balances exactly the horizontal component of the centrifugal force directed toward the equator (figure 11).

If there are no unbalanced horizontal forces acting, the free surface of a dish of

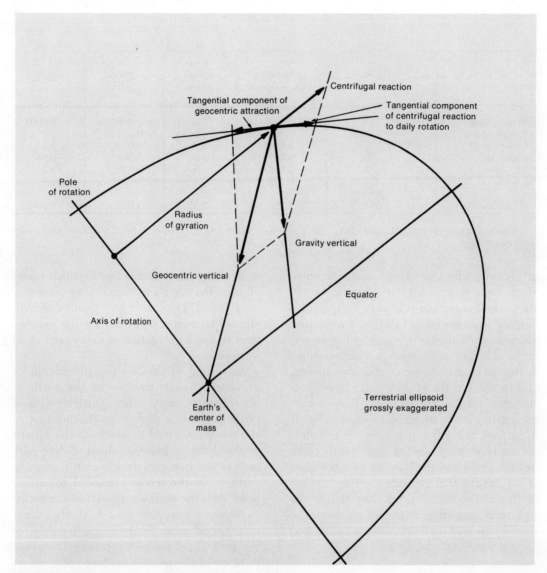

Figure 11 *Relationship of geocentric to plumb-line vertical.*

water will come to rest parallel with the terrestrial ellipsoid, and a plumb line will hang at right angles to it. This means that owing to rotational ellipticity, the direction of *gravity*—the resultant of Newtonian attraction and centrifugal force—differs from the line directed toward the geometrical center of the earth everywhere except at the poles and on the equator of the earth. This difference in direction is greatest at latitude 45°, where it amounts to about 11′ of arc. It also means that the acceleration of gravity will decrease equatorward because of the combined effects of the increase of distance of the surface of the earth from its center and the increased radius of gyration of points increasingly close to the equator.

Clairault showed in 1743 that the acceleration of gravity varies, to a first approximation, as the square of the sine of the latitude. The average reduction of the acceleration of gravity between the poles and the equator is 3.38 cm/sec², or about 0.3% of g_{90}. Local anomalies of g have importance in many precise physical measurements. Occasionally corrections may also be applied for the still smaller but time-dependent forces of lunar and solar gravitational attraction.

Because of the ellipsoidal figure of the earth, distances between points on its surface are not related to the angular separation of points by simple spherical equivalence. Instead of the shortest distance between any two points on the earth being an arc segment of a great circle, it is a segment of some other curve, a *geodesic*. A geodesic —the shortest distance between two points on a geoid—can range from nearly a circle when measured along the equator to nearly an ellipse when measured along a meridian. Study of the relationships of such curves between points on the earth's surface to their astronomical latitudes and longitudes and horizontal distances actually chained out between them is the concern of *geodesy*.

From geodetic studies of the shape of the earth, it has been learned that the local differences in the density of the rocky materials of the crust cause small anomalies in the acceleration of gravity and of the direction of local vertical. If the earth were flooded with motionless water, the surface of the water would be seen to have minor bulges and depressions. This equilibrium surface would depart from the ideal ellipsoid quite noticeably in some places (about 30 meters in the northern Indian Ocean) and would represent the true figure of the earth—the *geoid*. The geoid is a surface which lies at a variety of distances from the nominal center of the earth. But because of gravity anomalies and the rotational ellipticity of the earth, it would require an exactly equal expenditure of physical work against gravity to reach any point on the geoid from the nominal center of the earth. The geoid is, therefore, a surface which has uniform gravity potential above the geocenter: a surface of constant *geopotential*. Geopotential surfaces are level. There are enveloping the earth as many level surfaces of constant geopotential as one may choose to specify, but they never intersect and are rarely parallel.

A fluid particle on any geopotential surface will show no tendency to move unless acted on by some unbalanced force. Such forces may arise from thermal disturbances of hydrostatic equilibrium which tends to be restored by motions developed under the earth's gravity or, in the case of tides, from the action of the external gravitational fields of the sun and moon. These latter forces take on a variety of angular relationships having periodic changes and limits that are well known in terms of the rotation rates and orbital motions of the earth and moon.

XIV

THE OCEAN COVERS the greatest portion of the earth's surface. Its deep trenches are the largest features known, and some of its mountains are the highest on earth. The greatest amount of life on our planet lives in the sea. In addition, the seas contain roughly 2700 times more water than is contained in all freshwater impoundments.

Seawater has been defined as a dilute solution of almost everything. Over eons of time, the sea has collected in its basin all the elements that have been eroded from the continents, transported by rivers and brought down in solution to the sea. It has also collected solid and gaseous materials ejected from underwater and surface volcanoes, debris blown across it from land, meteoric material and material coming from marine biological activity. It was once estimated that if all the dissolved material in the oceans was removed and spread over land it would make a layer more than 500 feet thick.

The following selection by William S. von Arx describes the physical properties of seawater. Temperature, pressure and concentration of salt are considered in detail, along with mechanisms and fundamental processes that take place in seawater. While much of the selection will have its greatest appeal to the serious student of oceanography, the general reader will find fascination in reading about the basic composition and the gigantic mixing process that goes on in the saltwater portion of our planet.

Characteristics of Sea Water

Reprinted by permission of the publisher from William S. von Arx, *An Introduction to Physical Oceanography* (Reading, Mass.: Addison-Wesley Publishing Company, Inc., 1962), pp. 118-137.

SEA WATER is about 2700 times more abundant on the earth than impounded fresh water. The physical properties of sea water are different from those of fresh water, because they vary not only with temperature and pressure but with the concentration of salt. The temperature and the salt concentration of sea water undergo change mainly at the sea surface where the ocean interacts with the atmosphere. Transpiration of water through the sea surface, radiative exchange with the atmosphere, and mechanisms which mix newly conditioned surface water into the volume of the ocean are fundamental processes that are strongly influenced by the physical nature of sea water itself.

A meaningful description of the physical properties of sea water cannot always be given out of context with the natural situation. For example, where small bubbles, silt, or microorganisms are dispersed in natural waters transparency is altered, and where the sea surface is white-capped (or frozen) the ability of the oceans to exchange water vapor and other gases and to emit and absorb radiant energy is markedly changed. But certain other integral properties can be specified reasonably well for a usefully wide range of conditions. Among the most important of these properties is density.

Density

The density of sea water is determined by its total salt content s, its temperature t, and to a lesser degree by its compression under p, the burden of water and air above it. The average density, ρ, of sea water is near 1.025 gm/cm³. If a given sample has a density of 1.02523, the significant part of this number is generally in and beyond the third decimal. Therefore the convention has been adopted that in place of the density $\rho_{s,t,p}$, a quantity $\sigma_{s,t,p}$ be used. This is defined as follows:

$$\sigma_{s,t,p} = (\rho_{s,t,p} - 1)1000.$$

In this way $\rho_{s,t,p} = 1.02523$ gm/cm³ becomes $\sigma_{s,t,p} = 25.23$, with the units of measurement given by implication.

The density of sea water *in situ* is usually required to be known to an accuracy of 10^{-5}. At the present time there are no direct means for measuring density *in situ*, although interesting possibilities have been proposed. . . . Deductions of this quantity from the equations of state rely on empirical knowledge of the coefficients of thermal expansion of sea water, as well as on knowledge of saline contraction and isothermal compressibility. Because of nonlinear interactions, each of these is a somewhat imperfectly known function of the ambient temperature, salinity, and pressure.

For simplicity it is often assumed in dynamical oceanography that the buoyancy of a parcel of sea water is unchanged relative to its surroundings when the hydrostatic pressure on both the parcel and its surroundings is changed by the same amount. This is to say that the work done in moving the parcel from one level to another is, to a first approximation, independent of the absolute value of hydrostatic pressure change.

In considering the stability of a water column, it is convenient to be in a position to say whether a displaced parcel will be heavier or lighter (figure 1) than its surroundings from consideration of only its observed temperature and equivalent salt concentration. With this object in view, the density of sea water is often expressed as the quantity $\sigma_{s,t,0}$ (usually abbreviated σ_t and pronounced "sigma-tee"), which is the density of a parcel after the pressure has been reduced to one atmosphere, that is, brought to the sea surface. This operation neglects adiabatic effects, so that σ_t differs from *potential density* by this very small amount.

Salinity

Sea water is a very complex solution of organic and inorganic salts derived over the course of geologic time from the solu-

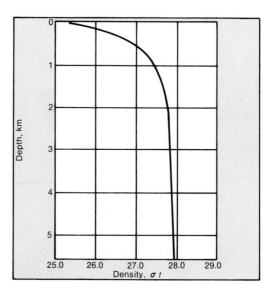

Figure 1 *Schematic diagram of the change in density with depth in the ocean.*

tion of rocks, the gaseous effusion of volcanoes, biological activity, and probably to a far lesser extent from meteoritic material in the earth's atmosphere. The salinity of sea water has been defined as "the total amount of solid material in grams contained in one kilogram of sea water when all the carbonate has been converted to oxide, the bromine and iodine replaced by chlorine, and all organic matter completely oxidized."[1] The numerical value of salinity defined in this manner is slightly lower than the amount of dissolved solids in grams per kilogram. The concentration of dissolved materials in sea water is measured most sensitively by its electrical conductivity, but chemical analysis is of both basic and historical interest.

Over the years a large number of samples of ocean water from different parts of the world ocean have been analyzed completely, and these show that regardless of the absolute concentrations of the individual constituents (see tables 1 and 2), the relative proportions of the major constituents are nearly constant. (The composition of

TABLE 1. The 42 Most Abundant Elements in Sea Water, in Percent by Weight[*]

Oxygen	85.89			Barium	1	$\times 10^{-6}$
Hydrogen	10.82			Zinc	5	$\times 10^{-7}$
Chlorine	1.90			Manganese	5	$\times 10^{-7}$
Sodium	1.06			Lead	4	$\times 10^{-7}$
Magnesium	0.13			Iron	2	$\times 10^{-7}$
Sulphur	0.088			Cesium	2	$\times 10^{-7}$
Calcium	0.040			Uranium	1.5	$\times 10^{-7}$
Potassium	0.038			Selenium	1	$\times 10^{-7}$
Bromine	6.5	$\times 10^{-3}$		Thorium	5	$\times 10^{-8}$
Carbon	2.8	$\times 10^{-3}$		Molybdenum	5	$\times 10^{-8}$
Strontium	1.3	$\times 10^{-3}$		Cerium	4	$\times 10^{-8}$
Boron	4.8	$\times 10^{-4}$		Silver	3	$\times 10^{-8}$
Silicon	2	$\times 10^{-4}$		Vanadium	3	$\times 10^{-8}$
Fluorine	1.4	$\times 10^{-4}$		Lanthanum	3	$\times 10^{-8}$
Nitrogen	0.3−7	$\times 10^{-5}$		Yttrium	3	$\times 10^{-8}$
Rubidium	2	$\times 10^{-5}$		Copper	2	$\times 10^{-8}$
Lithium	1.2	$\times 10^{-5}$		Nickel	1	$\times 10^{-8}$
Aluminum	1	$\times 10^{-5}$		Scandium	4	$\times 10^{-9}$
Phosphorus	5	$\times 10^{-6}$		Mercury	3	$\times 10^{-9}$
Iodine	5	$\times 10^{-6}$		Gold	4	$\times 10^{-10}$
Arsenic	1.5	$\times 10^{-6}$		Radium	7	$\times 10^{-15}$

[*]Victor M. Goldschmidt, 1954, p. 49, *Geochemistry.* **By permission of The Clarendon Press, Oxford.**

TABLE 2. W. Dittmar's (1884) values for the major constituents of sea water, [*] in percent by weight.

Cl^-	55.04	Mg^{++}	3.69
Br^-	0.19	Ca^{++}	1.16
SO_4^{--}	7.68	Sr^{++}	0.04
HCO_3^-	0.41	K^+	1.10
F^-	0.00+	Na^+	30.61
H_3BO_3	0.07		

[*]These values are corrected by Lyman and Fleming for re-evaluation of atomic weight. See J. Lyman and R. H. Fleming, 1940, *J. Mar. Res.,* 3:134-146; H. W. Sverdrup, *et al.,* 1942, p. 166. *The Oceans,* New York: Prentice-Hall.

salts from interior seas, such as the Caspian, Dead, and Salton Seas and the Great Salt Lake, differs from one sea to the other and from the composition of salts in the world oceans.) Thus it is possible to estimate the total salt content of sea water from measurements of the concentration of only one constituent, usually the chloride ion.

The chloride ion concentration in sea water can be measured by chemical titration against a standard solution of silver nitrate which yields a conspicuous precipitate of silver chloride. (The procedures used for the chemical titration of the chlorides in sea water generally follow Oxner's directions for implementing the method originally described by Martin Knudsen. Knudsen's *Hydrographical Tables,* 1901, 2nd ed., 1931, Copenhagen: G.E.C. GAD, London: Williams & Norgate, are still widely used for conversion of the measured chloride into equivalent total salt content.) The silver nitrate solution is first standardized against "normal water" prepared by the Hydrographical Laboratories in Copenhagen, or alternatively, since 1940, against American standard sea water prepared by F. M. Soule and C. A. Barnes at Woods Hole Oceanographic Institution. This has been carefully compared with the world standard Copenhagen water.

The relation between salinity and chlorinity, according to Knudsen (1901), is

$$\text{Salinity} = 0.03 + 1.805 \times \text{chlorinity}.$$

Both salinity and chlorinity are expressed in parts per thousand, denoted by ‰ Chlorinity given in parts per thousand expresses the mass of chlorine, bromine, and iodine in one thousand grams of sea-water solution, assuming that the iodine and bromine have been replaced by chlorine. (Since this definition of chlorinity gives numerical values which change with each refinement of the values of atomic weights, a new definition has been given which is independent of such changes. Chlorinity in grams per kilogram of sea water is identical with the mass in grams of "atomic weight silver" just needed to precipitate the halogens in a 0.3285233-kgm sample of sea water.) By chemical means it is possible to determine the concentration of chlorides to an accuracy of ±0.01‰. When the chlorinity is transformed into "salinity," the uncertainty rises to ±0.02 ‰. Recently, potentiometric titrations of total salts through their effects on the conductivity of sea water have begun to be more widely used. These lead to improved discrimination between samples and reproducibility of measurements

on the same sample, but still require translation into salinity units.

As early as 1922 F. Wenner designed a conductivity bridge which can be operated on shipboard and which has been used ever since by the U.S. Coast Guard in the work of the International Ice Patrol. The Wenner bridge is reported to be capable of discriminating salinity with a reproducibility of ±0.005 ‰, a significant improvement over that obtained by chemical titration.

The bridge contains two essentially identical conductivity cells. In one of these is placed a sample of standard sea water, in the other a sample of the unknown. When the temperature of the standard and unknown samples has been equalized, the impedance of the known and unknown cells is matched by means of suitable resistors and correcting capacitors. The null point of the measurement is indicated to the operator by the silencing of a 1000-cps tone when the two variable arms of the bridge are in balance. The Wenner design has not been used extensively, perhaps because of a reluctance on the part of oceanographers to deal with the difficulties so often encountered at sea in maintaining sensitive electrical equipment in working order. . . .

The Schleicher-Bradshaw "salinometer" is like the Wenner bridge in that two cells are used, one containing a standard and the other an unknown sample of sea water; but the instrument is modernized in that the balances are obtained through a phase-sensitive servo-amplifier after rough adjustments have been made manually. The circuit also employs a 1-ke input to the bridge, but the output is fed to a phase detector similar to the chopper amplifiers used in many modern recording potentiometers. The output of the amplifier causes a small motor to turn in one direction or the other to adjust the fine balance of the resistive component of the bridge circuit. Small inequalities in capacitance of the cells containing the standard and un-known sea water samples are nulled by land. The Schleicher-Bradshaw salinometer requires a smaller water sample than the Wenner bridge and therefore comes to temperature equilibrium more quickly but with essentially the same accuracy, ± 0.005 ‰ in salinity being maintained.

In a recent resurvey of the North Atlantic, it was shown that with the increased resolution of conductivity measurements, horizontal gradations of conductivity in the North Atlantic can be distinguished within oceanographic areas that chemical analysis for chlorinity had indicated to be composed of homogeneous layers. This is one of the few instances in geophysics where with increased resolving power the noise-to-signal ratio has been lowered rather than raised. Although the variability of conductivity as a function of position in the open oceans is less than the experimental scatter of chlorinities determined by chemical titration, it remains to be seen where the coherence level of these properties of sea water lies and, moreover, to discover the precise relationship between chlorinity, conductivity, and the total concentration of dissolved solids. The latter property is fundamental to indirect determinations of the density of sea water. Concentration of dissolved solids also influences the freezing point.

The concentration of salt in sea water, as estimated from chlorinity, is related to a depression of the freezing point below that of fresh water by an amount $\Delta T = 0.102710$ Cl, where Cl is the chlorinity per mille. At salinity 30 ‰ the freezing point is $-1.63°$C and at 35 ‰ sea water freezes at $-1.91°$C. (The vapor pressure of sea water is depressed along with the freezing point as is characteristic of aqueous solutions. Where e is the vapor pressure of sea water at a given salinity and e_0 is the vapor pressure of pure water at the same temperature, then $(e_0 - e)/e_0 = 0.537 \times$ salinity, according

to R. Witting, 1908, *Finnl, hydrogr.-biol. Untersuch.*, 2: 173.) Distilled water has a maximum density at 4°C, a little above the freezing point, but at a salinity of 24.70 ‰ the temperature of maximum density occurs at the freezing point, $-1.332°$C. Since sea water generally contains more salt than this, freezing usually occurs before the water has cooled sufficiently to attain maximum density. (The specific heat of sea water is slightly less than that of pure water, but the latent heats of fusion and vaporization are nearly the same because the salts are left behind in the evaporation process and excluded by freezing. The molecular thermal conductivity of sea water is also only slightly less than that of pure water at the same temperature, but its electrical conductivity is vastly greater. At 0°C sea water of salinity 35 ‰ has an electrical conductivity near 0.029 mho/cm, and at 30°C the same water has a conductivity near 0.058 mho/cm. Electrical conductivity tends to zero as salinity approaches zero.)

Temperature-Salinity Diagram

With the establishment of systematic, descriptive oceanography since the time of the *Challenger* expedition, numerous separate observations of the temperature and salinity of the oceans at many depths have been accumulated. In the open sea the salinities of water may range from about 33 ‰ to 36 ‰, while the corresponding temperatures may range from as little as $-1°$C to about 30°C. From tabulations of temperature and salinity data, it can be shown that certain regions of the oceans possess characteristic associations of salinity and temperature both by area and in the vertical, and that in general the density of the sea becomes less with elevation above the bottom. In 1916 Bjørn Helland-Hansen proposed that these variables be correlated by means of a *temperature-*

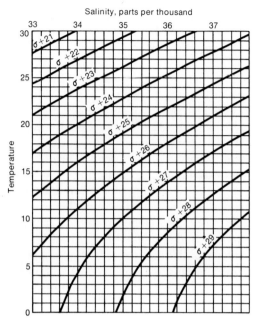

Figure 2 *Temperature-salinity sigma-T grid.*

salinity diagram (figure 2) in which the salinity of the sea water sample is plotted with increasing values toward the right, and the temperature of the same sample is plotted on a vertical scale with values increasing upward. When many separate observations of temperature and salinity of various geographical areas are plotted on this kind of diagram, it is not unusual for the points to fall in groups to the extent that oceanic areas and layers can be distinguished from one another as *water masses.* The principal layers of water having characteristic associations of salinity and temperature can be represented on the *T-S* diagram by a single point. These points define *water types.*

The *T-S* diagram has further uses in that with knowledge of the temperature and salinity of water at atmospheric pressure, σ_t is also specified. At constant pressure the density of sea water increases systematically with an increase of salinity and with a

decrease in temperature. Therefore, on a *T-S* diagram it is possible to rule a grid of lines of constant σ_t. Lines of equal σ_t will tend to slope upward from left to right across the *T-S* diagram. A change of salinity of 1 ‰ usually produces a larger change in the σ_t of sea water than a change of temperature of 1°C.

The lines of equal σ_t shown in figure 2 are slightly curved downward, as well as being inclined to the coordinate axes. Thus when two water types of different salinity and temperature lie side by side on the ocean surface and have precisely the same density, their mixture will be represented by a point on the straight line joining their positions in the *T-S* diagram. Since this point must lie on the concave side of the σ_t line, the mixture must be slightly more dense than either of the two parent water types and tend to sink. Sinking due to this mixing process is known as *caballing.* Caballing is presumed (but not yet demonstrated) to occur at significant rates mainly in high northern latitudes where there is but little change in water properties with depth, a condition which perhaps bears testimony to the effectiveness of the process.

Elsewhere in the modern oceans both salinity and temperature tend to decrease with increasing depth, so that water of higher σ_t and potential density is found at the lower levels. Because of this circumstance there is a remarkable possibility that sustained motion would occur in a vertical tube embedded in the ocean. If the tube were to extend from the relatively low density surface water to deep water of higher density and if water from the lower layer were pumped to the surface, the flow would continue when the pump was disconnected. Flow would be sustained because the vertical tube would carry the salt without change of concentration from the deeper level to the surface but would permit sufficient heat transfer to enable the water flowing upward in the tube to come to thermal equilibrium with its surroundings. Thus the relatively fresh but cold water from the depths would arrive at the surface as relatively fresh but warm water less dense than the saltier water of the same temperature surrounding the top of the tube. The buoyancy of the warmed deep water would permit the flow to continue for as long as suitably contrasting water types were maintained on the earth or until the tube crumbled with age or became choked with sessile organisms.

If the initial pumping action were directed downward, the salt but warm surface water would be carried to a depth where the surrounding deep water is cooler but fresher. With the attendant loss of heat on the way down, the surface water in the tube would be saltier than the water in its environment, so that it would continue to flow downward without further assistance. In the central North Atlantic a tube 2000 meters long might develop a pressure head of as much as two meters. Flow rates for tubes have been estimated by Groves. Stern has shown that convective filaments actually develop in the absence of any confining tubes because the rate of diffusion of salt in the ocean is about 110 times smaller than that of heat.

A demonstration of the first of these effects has been made on a laboratory scale using a graduated cylinder containing a schematic ocean in which a vertical metal tube is used to define the moving column of water. In this model the flow continues until the conditions of the experiment break down. In Stern's experiment the ocean is simulated in a large aquarium in which hot salt water dyed with fountain-pen ink is made to float over cold, clear fresh water. Vertical filaments develop across the interface within an hour. These suggest a new mechanism for vertical mixing in the oceans which is independent

of the large-scale overturning circulations.

Adiabatic Effects

As a water parcel is moved upward or downward in the ocean, its temperature varies slightly with the amount of compression. Although the compressibility of water is less than that of steel, increasing hydrostatic pressure causes an increase in the temperature of water. This adiabatic effect of pressure change was shown by Lord Kelvin to be approximately

$$\delta T = \frac{Te}{JC_p} g \ \delta h,$$

where C_p is the specific heat at constant pressure (a function of temperature), T is the absolute temperature, g is the acceleration due to gravity, e is the coefficient of thermal expansion (a function of salinity), J is the mechanical equivalent of heat, and δh is the vertical displacement of a unit mass. Kelvin's formula for the adiabatic effect of increasing pressure on sea water shows that the temperature rises approximately 0.03°C per 1000 decibars increase of pressure, not a very important amount.

Potential temperature, θ, is defined as $T - \delta T$, where T is the temperature of the water under the hydrostatic pressure prevailing at its place in the water column, and δT is the adiabatic temperature change due to lifting the parcel without exchange of heat with its environment to the pressure at the sea surface. In the very deepest part of the ocean, such as in the trenches flanking island arcs, it can be shown that the potential temperature of the water is virtually uniform from the depth of the surrounding ocean floor to the bottom of the trench, even though the actual temperature increases somewhat with depth. A case of this sort is shown in figure 3 representing a sounding in the Philippine trench made during the *Galathea* expedition of 1950-52.

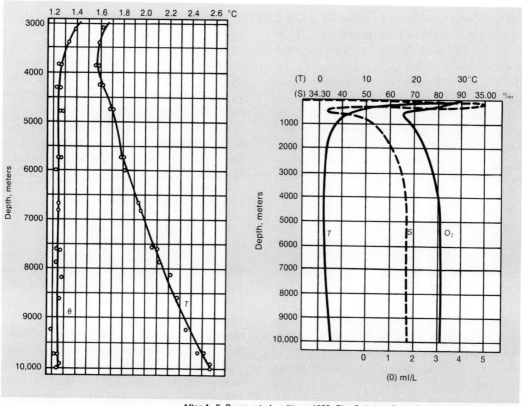

After A. F. Brunn, et al., editors, 1956, *The Galathea Deep Sea Expedition, 1950-1952,*
by permission of Macmillan, New York, and Allen and Unwin, London

Figure 3 *Temperature, salinity, and oxygen content in the Philippine trench, θ is the potential temperature.*

One can see in this figure that the actual temperature increases steadily with depth below the 4000-meter level of the surrounding ocean floor, while the salinity remains constant. On the other hand, the fact that the potential temperature between about 4000 meters and about 10,000 meters is effectively constant suggests that there is convective overturning in the trench. Adiabatic warming and cooling due to vertical motions of sea water have been observed only in relatively deep and confined spaces, such as the ocean trenches in the Arctic and European mediterranean basins and parts of the Red Sea, probably because the effect is slight enough to be easily destroyed in the presence of even very weak advection.

Adiabatic effects of a more instantaneous character also play a part in the propagation of compressional (sound) waves in the ocean, but since there is an adiabatic rise and fall of water temperature with the passage of a symmetrical compressional wave, these small effects essentially cancel out and do not influence in important ways the direction of propagation or energy of the wave front. The path of compressional waves in water is therefore governed by Snell's law of refraction. . . . (The acoustic index of refraction of the ocean may be generally lower in the surface layers than at mid-depths owing to the decrease of temperature with depth, so that compressional waves emitted near the surface are on the average bent downward. Below mid-depths the index of refraction is decreased by the increase of pressure by more than the amount it is increased with decreasing temperature. The net effect is to cause compressional waves emitted below mid-depths to be bent upward. The focusing effect of the water column on compressional waves emitted at mid-depths provides a channel or wave guide permitting compressional waves of acoustic frequencies to be transmitted over extraordinarily long ranges, sometimes several thousand of miles.)

Stratification

Owing to the influence of gravity and buoyancy forces, there is a tendency for dense parcels of water to sink, and for less dense parcels to rise toward the surface of the oceans. Ultimately, within each water column, a more or less stable vertical gradient of density is established. While a stably stratified water column may often be cooler at the bottom than at the top, it may also be fresher at the bottom. The balance of the opposing effects of increasing salinity and of increasing temperature on density may cause the separate gradients of salinity and temperature in the vertical to assume apparently unstable configurations in what is actually a stably stratified column from the standpoint of the vertical distribution of density.

The usually gentle vertical gradients of salinity and temperature in the oceans may sometimes be steepened in zones delimited by levels that are closely spaced relative to the total depth. In these layers the vertical gradients of temperature or salinity may be sharply graded from the deep-water regime to that of the surface-layer regime. A steep vertical gradient of temperature in an otherwise gently graded sounding is called a *thermocline*. In the oceans there

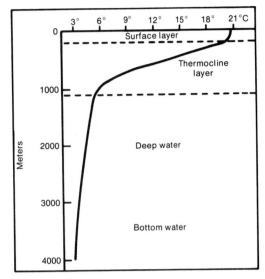

Figure 4 *The vertical subdivisions of the ocean.*

is a widespread *main* or *permanent thermocline* (figure 4) which lies deep enough to be almost unaffected by the annual cycle of seasons. In contrast to this there is sometimes a shallower thermocline that comes and goes with the seasons and is therefore referred to as a *seasonal thermocline*. Along with the temperature transition in a thermocline, there may be locally steepened vertical gradients of salinity and density, referred to as *haloclines* and *pycnoclines*, respectively. The physical mechanisms which form and maintain these transition layers are thought to be related to a balance of the downward diffusion of heat and salt-enriched water conditioned at the surface against the upward motion of fresher and cooler water from the ocean depths. (The processes maintaining the permanent thermocline are intimately connected with the problem of the general circulation of the oceans.)

The layering of the water types in the volume of the ocean may take two different forms: barotropic or baroclinic stratification. In a *barotropic* ocean (figure 5) the surfaces

Barotropic mode. Density, ρ, is a function of pressure p, alone, hence isobaric and isopycnal surfaces do not intersect. The fluid can be motionless when isobaric surfaces coincide with geopotential surfaces.

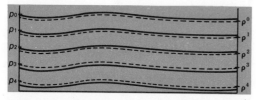

Baroclinic mode. Isobaric and isopycnal surfaces intersect. A baroclinic fluid cannot remain motionless.

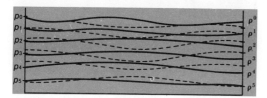

Figure 5 *Ocean stratification.*

of equal pressure (isobaric surfaces) lie parallel to surfaces of uniform density (isopycnal surfaces), and these in turn may lie parallel to the sea surface. When a barotropic ocean is at rest, the isobaric and isopycnal surfaces are parallel with geopotential surfaces. But when there is geostrophic motion accompanying the barotropic condition, the isobaric and isopycnal surfaces, provided that they remain parallel, may be inclined to geopotential surfaces. Barotropic stratification is not destroyed by regionally uniform fields of parallel force, such as those producing the astronomical tide and on a smaller scale those accompanying a widespread change of barometric pressure. In cases where such force fields are suddenly applied and some redistribution of mass is required to achieve equilibrium, the period of readjustment is virtually complete in 12 pendulum hours. Where, however, the field of force establishes steady patterns of current, the period of barotropic equilibration is on the order of 12 to 14 days in middle latitudes.

In contrast to this, the *baroclinic* condition of stratification exists when isobaric surfaces are inclined to isopycnal surfaces. Both may be inclined to geopotential surfaces. (The effects of internal waves are to be overlooked in this connection.) The situation is illustrated by the unequal stands of liquid level in a U-tube when the two arms contain a succession of fluids of differently graduated densities. The baroclinic structure of the oceans is especially pronounced in the upper 500 to 1000 meters of depth. Below these levels the deeper layers approach the barotropic condition.

Where there is sustained baroclinicity there is also water motion, for where isobaric surfaces are inclined there is a horizontal gradient of pressure. Since the regional inequalities of density producing baroclinic structures are usually maintained by persistent external influences, such as climate, the flow tends to be geostrophic. Indeed the geostrophic assumption is often made the basis for interpreting the relationship between the steady component of the primary ocean circulation and the distribution of water characteristics. Because of the great reservoirs of water in each of the oceanic water masses, it takes tens or even hundreds of years for appreciable changes to develop in the baroclinic structure of the major oceanic regions of the earth. This is partly because sea water is not easily penetrated by the sun's light and heat, and yet has an enormous capacity for heat storage.

Heat Capacity

Both the near and especially the far infrared bands of solar radiation are rapidly absorbed in the first few millimeters of water depth. Visible light is more gradually transformed into heat, because it penetrates far more deeply into the sea before being absorbed. In the presence of waves and currents, both the shallow and deep radiant heating of the sea is mixed downward within a few hours to a depth which we shall say for convenience is on the order of 100 meters under most circumstances. On land, solar radiation is absorbed by a very thin layer of material and carried downward by relatively slow processes of thermal conduction. It is of interest to compare the temperature changes in the two cases.

With the assumption that solar radiation is absorbed at the same rate on land and sea, the rise in temperature per unit time, dT/dt, of a cubic centimeter of water at the sea surface can be calculated and compared with the rise in temperature of a cubic centimeter of bare rock under like conditions with the aid of the equation

$$\frac{dT}{dt} = \frac{1}{\rho C_1} \frac{dH}{dt}$$

Let dH/dt equal 1 gm·cal/min/cm² and assume that ρ, the density of rock, is 2.5 gm/cm³ while that of sea water is 1 gm/cm³, that the specific heat of C_ρ of rock is 0.2 cal/gm/°C while that of sea water is 1 cal/gm/°C. (Actually the specific heat of sea water is lower than that of fresh water.) Then we find that if the rock is heated without reflection to a depth of 1 cm, the rate of temperature rise of the rock will be 2°C/min. In the oceans, however, and again neglecting reflection, the rate of temperature rise is 1°C/min, which is not strikingly less until it is considered that the sea mixes its heat downward. The initial centimeter of heated water therefore shares its heat content with a water column perhaps 100 meters deep. Thus the average temperature rise in the sea surface is 10^{-4}°C/min. From this we are led to conclude that the oceans are warmed only very slowly and, compared with land, can accommodate a very large amount of heat at a given surface temperature because of vertical mixing. Only on the calmest days,

when vertical mixing is slight enough to permit a shallow thermocline to develop, will the afternoon surface temperature of the sea rise a degree or two above the temperature of the water a few meters below the surface.

Penetration of Visible Light

Sunlight incident upon a glassy smooth ocean is partly reflected and the balance is refracted, scattered, or absorbed. The amount of visible light reflected varies with the angle of incidence, as shown in table 3. The variability of the reflection coefficient of smooth water with the angle of incidence is not shared by the rocky, grassy, or forest-covered areas of the earth. However, in the normally ruffled or wavy condition of the sea the angle of incidence is highly varied, and thus absorption continues during the day unless foam is sufficiently abundant to increase the reflection coefficient of the sea surface. It should also be recognized that part of the incoming solar radiation arrives as diffuse energy. On a clear day at noon about 85% of the radiation is direct and 15% is diffuse. When the sun is low in a clear sky, the proportion of scattered radiation is greater, being as much as 40%

TABLE 3	
Angle of incidence, degrees	Percent reflectivity
0	2.0
10	2.0
20	2.1
30	2.1
40	2.5
50	3.4
60	6.0
70	13.4
80	34.8
90	100.0

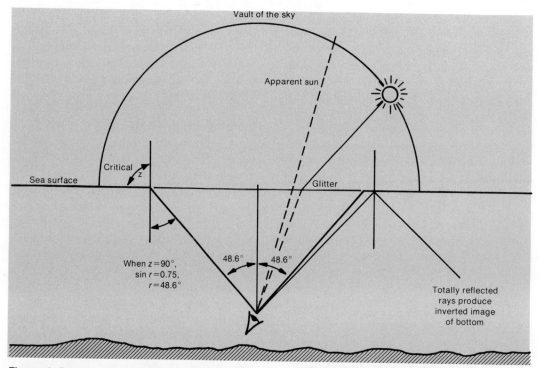

Figure 6 *Factors influencing the radiance of the sky as seen from a point beneath the surface of a glassy sea.*

of the total when the sun's altitude is 10 degrees.

Visible light striking a smooth sea surface in refracted downward toward the normal in accordance with Snell's law, which states that the ratio of the sine of the angle of incidence to the sine of the angle of refraction is the same as the ratio of the refractive indices of the two media. (The refractive index of sea water is a function of temperature, salinity, and pressure.) Thus viewed from beneath a glassy smooth sea surface (figure 6) the sun appears closer to the vertical than it appears when viewed above the sea surface; the horizon is seen at a zenith angle of about 48.6 degrees. The illuminated region overhead is the base of a cone having its apex centered on the observer's eye. This luminous circle can have the appearance of a manhole in perfectly calm weather. Beyond the edge of

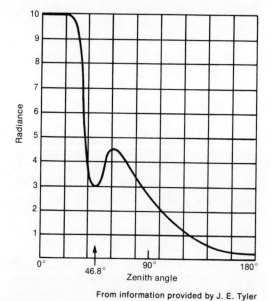

From information provided by J. E. Tyler

Figure 7 *Schematic diagram of the radiance reaching a point in the sea as a function of the zenith angle on an overcast day.*

the manhole, light from the bottom (and objects in the surrounding water) suffers a single reflection from the sea surface, producing an inverted image. Thus as one scans from the zenith to the horizontal just below the water surface, the light intensity falls off (as the reflection coefficient of the sea increases) to the critical angle where it reaches a minimum; beyond the critical angle the light intensity rises again to a secondary peak before falling off to a second minimum as one looks straight down (figure 7).

As one goes deeper in calm water the intensity of light reaching the eye dimin-ishes owing to attenuation through scattering and absorption in the water. The effect of these diffusing processes leads to a change in the direction of maximum radiance: from the direction of the refracted solar beam toward the vertical as the depth is increased. Thus at shallow depths, the sun appears as a bright spot in the manhole; while at greater depths the sun and the manhole become diffuse and the point of maximum radiance shifts more nearly overhead. At the same time there is absorption primarily of red light which causes the visual field to appear more and more blue-green in color. With increasing depth, the scatter-

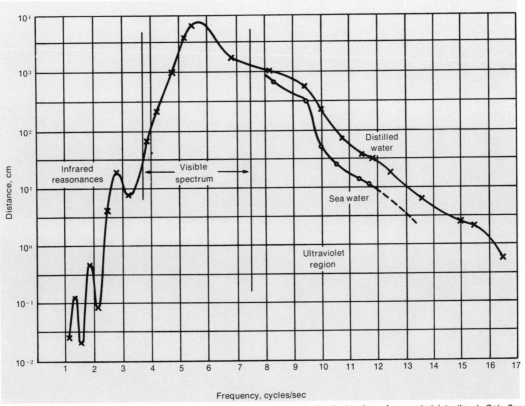

Composite curve drawn by L. A. Jacobsen from material in the *J. Opt. Soc. Am.*, Vol. 24 (1934), pp. 175-177; Vol. 29 (1939), pp. 43-55; Vol. 17 (1928), pp. 15-22

Figure 8 *Frequency versus distance for 90% attenuation.*

ing process causes the upward flux of light to contribute a large fraction of the total radiance reaching a point, so that when one looks down the water appears to glow. This effect can even be seen from above the surface. In very clear water in the open ocean the glow has a luminous but velvety cobalt-blue color which makes the phrase "wine-dark sea" take on more than literary significance.

The visible light penetrating the volume of the sea contains only a minor fraction of the total energy of sunlight but this can produce direct heating in the illuminated layer. Long wavelength radiation is strongly absorbed (figure 8). The very shallowness of long wave heating permits the oceans to distill large amounts of water (about one meter per year) into the lower atmosphere. This evaporative process tends

to charge the atmosphere with latent heat which is eventually released in a precipitation process at some other place on the earth.

The transport of fresh water by the atmosphere influences the salinity of the surface layers of the oceans and, through the redistribution of heat, alters the winds which tend to govern at least the surface circulations. These, in turn, produce further modification of the distribution of heat and of the atmospheric circulations, and so it goes. . . .

References

[1]C. Forch, M. Knudsen, and S. P. L. Sørensen, 1902, *K. danske vidensk. Selsk.*, 6, 12: 151 pp.

XV

THE ANCIENT ROMANS KNEW very little about water beneath the earth's surface. They built an imposing valley-spanning aquaduct system to carry stream and spring water from the distant Apennine Mountains to their great city. A perfectly adequate water system lay underfoot if they had only dug wells. Many other civilizations, however, utilized a knowledge of ground water. They dug elaborate wells and constructed complicated subterranean canals to trap a steady supply of water for their needs.

Many things happen to water that falls as rain or snow. Some evaporates back into the atmosphere, some runs on the surface in streams and some is picked up by plants and returned to the air by transpiration. Finally, some part of it soaks into the pores and cracks of the soil and into the rocks beneath the surface and becomes the ground water that is responsible for springs, wells, caves and some geysers.

The study of underground water is a special branch of geology which combines the efforts of geologists, hydraulicians, agronomists, chemists and physicists specializing in earth sciences. A noted geohydrologist, Roger J. M. De Wiest, discusses in the next selection the history of ground-water study—the early theories, modern developments, and importance to man of research and continued study in the field.

The Science of Subsurface Water

Scope of Topic

The study of subsurface water generally includes a consideration of its chemical and physical properties, geologic environment, natural movement, recovery, and utilization. For many years this subject has been called hydrogéologie by Belgian and French workers and hidrogeología by Latin American researchers. German scientists on the other hand defined the term hydrology as that part of the general science of water which relates specifically to the water below the surface. The tendency to restrict the term hydrology to the study of subsurface waters and to use terms such as hydrography and hydrometry to denote the study of surface waters existed also in the United States. As late as 1938, the Executive Committee of the International Association of Scientific Hydrology (IASH) recognized the use of the name hydrology for the branch dealing with underground waters (eaux souterraines) to distinguish from potamology (dealing with streams), limnology (study of lakes), and cryology (dealing with snow and ice).

It was Meinzer[1] who first suggested the term of "geohydrology" for the study of ground water, at a meeting of the IASH in 1939. Before him, Mead[2], hydraulic engineer and a past president of the American Society of Civil Engineers, had defined hydrogeology as the study of the laws of the occurrence and movement of subterranean waters. Engineers and geologists alike agree with him that "this must presuppose or include a sufficient study of general geology to give a comprehensive knowledge of the geological limitations which must be expected in hydrographic conditions and of the modifications due to geological changes." Mead stressed the special character of the study of "ground water as a geological agent, the understanding of which would contribute to attain a comprehension of the birth and growth of rivers and drainage systems." Meinzer subdivided the science of hydrology, which according to his definition dealt specifically with water completing the hydrologic cycle from the time it is precipitated upon the land until it is discharged into the sea or returned to the atmosphere, into surface hydrology and subterranean hydrology or geohydrology.

Obviously, some controversy has arisen as to the proper meaning of the words hydrogeology and geohydrology. Mead and Meinzer, authors of classical textbooks on hydrology, have used both terms to describe the same subdivision of hydrology. Moreover, many American geologists have followed the literal meaning of the word hydrogeology and have extended its usage to cover all studies, both of surface and subsurface water, which include a substantial amount of geologic orientation. The subject matter of this book, nevertheless, is confined to subsurface water; the title of the book has been chosen in conformity with Meinzer's definition and emphasizes the hydrology of ground water rather than its geological nature, according to the preface of the book. The knowledge of geohydrology is a basic requirement in the training of ground-water geologists and ground-water hydraulicians.

The best scientific research and professional work is often accomplished through combined efforts by geologists, hydraulicians, agronomists, chemists, and physicists specialized in the earth sciences. Cooperation has become imperative with the increasing complexity of the ground-water problems that remain to be solved and has been fostered in recent times by a better dissemination of scientific literature, avoiding thereby unnecessary duplication of research. Thus there is a common interest in the fundamentals of ground-water flow held by the hydrogeologist concerned with the evaluation of the safe yield of a ground-water basin and by the engineer in charge of drainage and irrigation projects. Principles of dispersion and diffusion in porous media applied by petroleum engineers in the study of the migration of gas and oil are also used in the analysis of salt water intrusion in coastal aquifers. The domain of fluid flow through porous media is not confined to that of rock and earth materials: mechanical engineers are interested in the heat exchange process associated with the movement of a gas through porous media; chemical engineers study the mass transfer of a gas from a mixture to a liquid solvent flowing in opposite sense through packed towers. Consequently, a vast body of technical literature dealing with the physics of the flow through porous media has become available to both hydrogeologists and geohydrologists.

History of Hydrogeology and Geohydrology

GROUND-WATER UTILIZATION

In the dry regions of Asia, the universal scarcity of water, the locally dense population, and the dominance of agriculture resulted in an early development of the art of constructing wells and infiltration galleries. Accounts of well water and well construction abound in ancient literature and are specially well known from the Biblical record of Genesis.

Well construction in the Near East was by man and animal power aided by hoists and primitive hand tools, despite great difficulties. A number of large-diameter wells, some large enough to accommodate paths for donkeys, attest both to the industry of the people and to the scarcity of water. These wells rarely exceed a depth of 50 meters. There is little evidence of technological advances in well drilling during historic time in this region despite the fact that Egyptians had perfected core drilling in rock as early as 3,000 B.C. This drilling was confined to stone quarry operations. Ancient Chinese, prolific in many inventions, were also responsible for the development of a churn drill for water wells, which, in principle, was almost identical to modern machines. The early machinery was largely of wood and powered by human hands. Through a slow drilling rate sustained for years, and even decades, these ancient people were able to achieve wells of amazing depths. Bowman[3] reports a depth of 1,200 meters and Tolman[4] a depth of 1,500 meters. The deepest holes, however, were drilled for brine and gas rather than for potable water. The same methods, only slightly modified during the past 1,500 years, are still used today in rural areas of Laos, Cambodia, Thailand, Burma, and China.

The greatest achievement in ground-water utilization by ancient peoples was in the construction of long infiltration galleries, or kanats, which collected water from alluvial fan deposits and soft sedimentary rock. These structures, commonly several kilometers long, collected water for both agricultural and municipal purposes. Kanats were probably used first more than 2,500 years ago in Iran; however, the technique of construction spread rapidly eastward to Afghanistan and westward to Egypt. One extensive kanat system built about the year 500 B.C. in Egypt is said to have irrigated 3,500 square kilometers of fertile land west of the Nile. Many kanats are still in use today in Iran and Afghanistan, the best known of which are in Iran on the alluvial fans of the Elburz Mountains.

Owing to a lack of early cultural contact with China, modern percussion methods of well drilling were developed more or less independently in Western Europe. The impetus for this development came largely from the discovery of flowing wells, first in Flanders about A.D. 1100, then a few decades later in eastern England and in northern Italy. One of the first wells was dug in A.D. 1126 by Carthusian monks from a convent near the village of Lillers. In Gonnehem, Flanders, near Bethune, four wells were drilled and were cased 11⅓ ft. above ground level so that they were able to

deliver water at sufficient height to drive a water mill. The wells were several hundred feet deep and tapped water under pressure from a formation consisting of fractured chalk that had its outcrop area in the higher plateaus of the Province of Artois. These and other similar wells in the region of Artois became so famous that flowing wells were eventually called artesian wells after the name of the region.

The widespread search for artesian water stimulated a rapid development of drilling techniques. Popular interest was so great in France that for a number of years the Royal and Central Society of Agriculture of France distributed annual medals and prizes to workers in the field, to authors, inventors, well-drillers, and to those who introduced these wells in new areas. Although drilling methods were more rapid and efficient in Europe than in China during the late eighteenth century, the depths of the wells rarely exceeded 300 meters. It was not until the end of the nineteenth century that the depths of water wells drilled by modern machinery exceeded the depths of the more primitive Chinese wells.

The methods of drilling for water have improved rapidly during the past 100 years, partly owing to knowledge borrowed from oil and gas drilling. The most significant single advance in drilling techniques has been the development of hydraulic rotary methods. Early rotary drilling was done with the aid of an outer casing; however, in about 1890 thick mud was found to be sufficient for holding up the walls of the hole, and the outer casing was no longer used. With this new efficiency and with the successful drilling of the Spindle Top oil field in Texas in 1901 by rotary methods, rotary drilling has steadily gained in popularity during the past 50 years.

The perfection of the deep-well turbine pump in the years between 1910 and 1930 added a further stimulus to the well-drilling industry. Prior to this time, deep wells were fitted with low-capacity piston pumps of poor efficiency. The new turbine pumps made irrigation by wells feasible in many areas hitherto underdeveloped for agriculture. The large production of these wells has placed a greater demand on the well-drilling industry for bigger and more permanent wells.

Although technology is still being borrowed from the oil industry, many innovations such as reverse rotary drilling, gravel envelope wells, and water-well cameras have come directly from the water-well industry itself.

THE ORIGIN OF SUBSURFACE WATER—EARLY THEORIES

When one considers the importance of ground water in the Oriental civilizations, it is strange that there is little record left concerning theories as to its origin. It remained for the inquisitive Greeks to speculate about such matters. Even though considerable thought was given by the Greeks to the origin of ground water, their contributions were surprisingly sterile, particularly in light of the amazing progress they made in philosophy and mathematics. One probable reason for the lack of progress in ground-water theory was the insistence of Plato and others that philosophy and science be more or less separated from their important contact with experimentation, field observation, and practical applications. Thus a wide gap was created between practice and theory. The significance of Greek thought is in the scientific dogma that it created for almost 2,000 years. The authority of Greek writings in the earth sciences reached a peak in the scholasticism of Albertus Magnus (A.D. 1206-1280) and Thomas Aquinas (A.D. 1225-1274) during the Middle Ages (roughly A.D. 1250-1450), but still persisted with considerable strength until a scant 200 years ago.

The Greeks were impressed with the large size of rivers in comparison with the observed runoff from heavy rains. They were also impressed by caves, sinks, and large springs characteristic of the limestone terrain which covers much of the Balkan Peninsula. The most common explanation for the origin of rivers was that they were fed from large springs, which in turn were fed by underground rivers or lakes nourished directly or indirectly by the ocean. Two problems confronted the early natural philosopher. (1) How did the ocean loose its salt? (2) How did ocean water rise from the level of the sea to springs high in the mountains?

Thales (640-546 B.C.), who was an Ionian philosopher of the School of Miletus, has been called the first true scientist. He taught that water was driven into the rocks by wind and that it was forced to the surface by rock pressure, whence it emerged as springs. Plato (427-347 B.C.), the great Athenian philosopher, conceived of one large underground cavern which is the source of all river water. Water was returned to the cavern from the ocean by various subsurface passages. The driving mechanism for this circulation was not fully explained. Krynine[5] has pointed out that the foregoing interpretation of Plato's ideas which influenced medieval science was probably not a correct interpretation of his more serious thoughts on the subject. Plato's "Critias" contains a description of the hydrologic cycle which is quite accurate. Although Aristotle (384-322 B.C.) was a student of Plato, he modified considerably Plato's concepts of the origin of ground water. Aristotle taught that ground water occurred in an intricate sponge-like system of underground openings and that water was discharged from these openings into springs. Water vapor which emanated from the interior of the earth contributes the greatest part of the spring water. Aristotle did, however, recognize that some cavern water originated from rainwater which had infiltrated into the ground and had entered the cavern in liquid form rather than as vapor.

The Romans generally followed Greek teachings in the sciences. Marcus Vitruvius, however, who lived about 15 B.C., made several original contributions to engineering and science. He is, perhaps, best known for his contributions to architecture, particularly in the acoustics of buildings. He was also one of the first persons to have a correct grasp of the hydrologic cycle. He taught that water from melting snow seeped into the ground in mountainous areas and appeared again at lower elevations as springs. In contrast, the famous Stoic philosopher, Lucius Annaeus Seneca (4 B.C.-A.D. 65) held essentially the same theory as Aristotle but denied the reality of infiltrating rainwater. The conclusions of Seneca were taken as positive proof for more than 1,500 years that rainfall was an insufficient source for spring water.

Bernard Palissy (1509-1589), French natural philosopher, was perhaps the first to have thorough modern views concerning the hydrologic cycle as reflected in the dialogue between "Theory" and "Practice" of his chapter "Des eaux et fontaines." Nevertheless many of the ideas of the Greeks and Romans prevailed until the end of the seventeenth century. Two of the most influential scientists of their time, Johannes Kepler (1571-1630), German astronomer, and Athanasius Kircher (1602-1680), German mathematician, elaborated greatly on the earlier ideas of Seneca and Aristotle. Kepler taught that the earth was similar to a large animal and that sea water was digested and that fresh water from springs was the end product of the earth's metabolism. The ideas of Kircher were exposed in his "Mundus Subterraneus," which was first printed in 1664 and soon became the standard reference work on geology for scholars of the seventeenth century. The work was ambitious in scope and unsurpassed in a display of spectacular imagination. Springs, which were fed by subterranean channels connected to the sea, were thought to issue from large caverns in mountains. Whirlpools, particularly the somewhat mystical Maelström off the coast of Norway, were thought to mark the positions of openings to the caverns in the sea bottom.

Between the dawn of scientific thinking and the end of the Renaissance, about A.D. 1600, little advance was made in hydrogeology and geohydrology. Five main facts were missed by all but a few early philosophers and scientists. (1) The earth does not contain a network of large interior caverns. (2) Although suction of the wind, capillary attraction, the forces of the waves, and other natural mechanisms exist to raise water against gravity, these mechanisms are insufficient to lift vast quantities of water in the earth's interior. (3) Sea water does not loose all its salt by infiltrating through soil. (4) Rainfall is sufficient to account for all water discharged by rivers and springs. (5) Rainfall infiltrates into the ground in large quantities.

THE FOUNDERS OF HYDROGEOLOGY AND GEOHYDROLOGY

The true source of river water was proved by two French scientists, Pierre Perrault (1608-1680), and Edmé Mariotte (1620-1684). Perrault measured rainfall in the Seine River basin for the years 1668, 1669, and 1670 and found the average to be 520 mm per year. He then estimated runoff from the basin and concluded that it was only one sixth of the total volume of rain, thus proving that rainfall was more than sufficient to account for all stream water. Studies of evaporation and capillary rise were also made by Perrault. He proved that capillary rise could never form a free body of water above the water table and that the height of capillary rise in sand was less than one meter. Mariotte measured the amount of infiltration of rainwater into a cellar at the Paris Observatory. He noted that this infiltration, as well as spring flow at other places, varied with the rainfall. He concluded, therefore, that springs were fed by rainwater which infiltrated into the ground. Mariotte's important contributions were published in Paris in 1690, after his death, and also as collected works[6] in Leiden in 1717. The latter contain Mariotte's essay "Du mouvement des eaux" (pp. 326-353), dealing with the properties of fluids, the origin of flowing wells, winds, storms and hurricanes, and other topics. Using the float method, Mariotte estimated the flow of the Seine River at the Pont Royal in Paris at 200,000 ft^3 per minute, or 1.05×10^{11} ft^3 per year, less than one sixth of the total annual precipitation on the basin that provides the runoff to the Seine upstream of Paris. "It was therefore evident, if one third of the precipitation evaporated from the ground," as Mariotte assumed, "and if one third remained in the earth, that there would be enough water left to sustain the flow of wells and rivers in the basin." Thus Mariotte verified Perrault's conclusions concerning the source of water for runoff. Several years later Edmund Halley (1656-1742), the famous British astronomer, published studies of evaporation from the Mediterranean Sea and concluded that this evaporation was able to account for all the water flowing into this sea by rivers, thus adding important data in support of the two French scientists.

Artesian wells have excited speculation since the days of the early Greeks, but correct explanations were not widely published until the first part of the eighteenth century. The first explanation which was mechanically correct was made by the brilliant Arabian philosopher al-Biruni (973-

1048). The best documented explanation came much later and was by Antonio Vallisnieri, president of the University of Padua, Italy, who published a paper in 1715 on the artesian water in northern Italy. He illustrated his paper with some of the earliest geologic cross sections, which were drawn for him by Johann Scheuchzer.[7]

Although his work was somewhat anticipated by Hagen and Poiseuille, Henry Darcy (1803-1858)[8] was the first person to state clearly the mathematical law which governs the flow of ground water. Darcy was a well-known French engineer whose main achievement was to develop a water supply for the city of Dijon, France. The development of his formula was the result of experimentation with filter sands and was presented in 1856 in an appendix of a report on the municipal water supply of Dijon. His report, however, resembled a scientific monograph on hydraulic engineering more than a present-day engineering report.

MODERN HYDROGEOLOGY
AND GEOHYDROLOGY

Developments during the past century have been along three more or less separate lines: (1) elaboration of the relation between geology and ground-water occurrences. (2) development of mathematical equations to describe the movement of water through rocks and unconsolidated sediments, and (3) the study of the chemistry of ground water, or hydrogeocehmistry.

The development of the relation between geology and ground-water occurrence is difficult to associate with individual names. In general, many geologists have contributed to specific problems. For example, the occurrence of ground water in areas of perennially frozen ground has been studied by a large number of Russian geologists. Many Dutch geologists have contributed to the understanding of ground water in coastal sand dunes. Japanese geologists and geophysicists have made numerous contributions to the understanding of hot springs. The English have made several contributions, one of which was an early application of geology by William Smith in 1827 to increase the water supply of Scarborough, England[9]. After a study of the local geology, he recommended that ground-water storage be increased by partially damming a spring. A. Daubrée[10] of France wrote one of the earliest general treatises on the geological aspects of ground water. For a specific example of modern contributions of an individual geologist the work of H. T. Stearns in the Hawaiian Islands can be cited. This work gives an excellent description of the relation between volcanic rocks and the occurrence of ground water. The work of W. M. Davis and J. H. Bretz on the formation of limestone caverns is another good example. Still another example is the work of DuToit on the consolidated rocks of the Union of South Africa. Despite the great number of geologists that could be cited, one man, O. C. Meinzer, stands out as the most important. Although he contributed to methods of making ground-water inventories and to the theory of artesian flow, and stressed the importance of phreatophytes, his main contribution was organizing the science of ground water[11]. He analyzed, defined, and welded together the various facets of the new branch of earth science largely between the years of 1920 and 1940, when he was a member of the United States Geological Survey.

Advances in ground-water hydraulics can be more easily identified with individual people because specific formulas are commonly published rather than generalized concepts which are so important in classical geology. Jules Dupuit[12], of France, was the first scientist to develop a formula for the flow of water into a well. This work was published only seven years after Darcy's monograph, yet successfully utilized Darcy's law. In 1870 Adolph Thiem[13], of Germany, modified Dupuit's formula so that he could actually compute the hydraulic characteristics of an aquifer by pumping a well and observing the effects in other wells in the vicinity. For many years Thiem continued to perfect his method and to apply it to various field situations. Modern methods of higher mathematics were first applied extensively to ground-water flow by Philip Forchheimer[14], of Austria, in 1886. He introduced the concept of equipotential surfaces and their relation to streamlines. He was also the first to apply Laplace's equation and the method of images. In the United States, C. A. Slichter[15] published similar work thirteen years later. Slichter developed his ideas independently of Forchheimer.

A great advance was made in the quantitative analysis of ground-water flow in 1935 when C. V. Theis introduced an equation for nonsteady state flow to a well. A formula had been developed seven years earlier in Germany by Herman Weber; nevertheless, the formula of Theis has proved to be of much greater utility. Theis' equation was based on an analogy with the heat flow, but a few years later C. E. Jacob derived the same expression through hydraulic considerations alone. In the past years Jacob and many other workers have improved the usefulness of Theis' basic equation by modifying it for a large number of boundary conditions.

The most significant contribution in recent times to the mathematical analysis of the movement of ground water has been made by Morris Muskat[16], whose book on fluid flow through porous media remained unchallenged and unmatched for years after it was originally published in 1937. In 1964 it is still a valuable reference work in teaching, and it will remain an indispensable tool in research for many years to come. Muskat wrote numerous original papers on the flow of subterranean fluids, providing a base upon which later research was founded and leading to stimulating discussions. Equally valuable was the work by M. King Hubbert[17] whose lucid thoughts on fundamental concepts of fluid flow in the ground reflect a deep understanding of the physics of the phenomenon. He derived Darcy's law from the Navier-Stokes equations and introduced the concept of force potential in his mathematical derivation, a concept more general and useful than that of velocity potential, which, strictly spoken, applies only when the fluid is water with constant physicochemical properties. The concept of force potential is at the base of Hubbert's work on immiscible displacement in multiphase systems and on hydrodynamical entrapment of petroleum.

The subject of ground water has attracted the attention of many Russian researchers; among them the names and contributions of Zhukovsky, pioneer of the air foil theory, and even more of Pavlovsky[18] are outstanding. Unfortunately, except for Polubarinova's book[19], little of this work has become available to the Western scientist in the form of unabridged translations into English. In the field of hydrogeology, Selin-Bekchurin[20] has been very prominent.

Chemical analyses of water have been routine for more than a century; however, the successful correlation of water chemistry with the hydrologic and geologic environments, or hydrogeochemistry, is a more recent development. Early attempts at geochemical interpretations were made by B. M. Lersch of Germany in 1864 and T. S. Hunt of Canada in 1865. Modern hydrogeochemical studies in North America started with the work of F. W. Clarke, done from about 1910 to 1925, and included a large number of chemical analyses of water with geochemical interpretations. Another early geochemist who made detailed studies of specific areas in the United States was Herman Stabler. His regional studies of water chemistry in the western United States have been excelled only during the past decade. Modern trends in hydrogeochemistry include exhaustive studies of chemical ratios, largely by Russian and French workers, the use of trace elements (to prospect for mineral deposits) in many countries, and detailed studies of various isotopes by workers in Japan, the United States, Russia, and many other countries. Hydrogeochemistry today is a subject of research and teaching, especially in some French and German Universities.

Hydrology and Human Affairs

Many aspects of hydrogeology and geohydrology are as yet of special interest only to scientists. Nevertheless it is a branch of the earth sciences which has in a large measure been born out of practical considerations. Indeed, many of the most important advances in hydrogeology and geohydrology today have been stimulated by studies designed to solve problems of great economic importance. This trend will probably continue, as the demand for water will undoubtedly increase with growing population and industrialization.

The development of modern household equipment, new industrial processes, and recent farming techniques have all increased the need for water. Water is used for washing, irrigation, cooling, to extinguish fires, as a solvent, and for countless other needs of modern society. The demands of an undeveloped agricultural society are only for a minimum amount of water. Without modern plumbing, one man can have sufficient water for drinking, for cooking, and for washing even if he is limited to only 20 liters (5 to 6 gal) per day. In a modern home, in contrast, a single bath can easily consume twice this quantity. With automatic washing machines, lawn

USDA photo

Well-drilling equipment on a farm in western Oklahoma, where the use of ground water for irrigating crops is turning parts of the old "dust bowl" into prosperous farmland. This farmer plans to drill six wells and install a central pumping unit to supply water to 80 acres. The system is costly but can prove profitable in an area where there is an adequate underground water supply but scanty rainfall and few streams.

sprinklers, and other water-consuming devices of modern living, many communities have an average consumption of more than 600 liters (165 gal) per person per day. If modern industry is taken into account, the water-production problems of even small cities become tremendous. For example, it commonly takes more than 10 liters of water to process one kilogram of meat, 100 liters to produce one kilogram of paper, and almost 200 liters to produce one kilogram of steel. Fortunately, a great amount of industrial water is not consumed and can be reused after proper treatment.

Modern agriculture consumes the largest amount of water. Many irrigated crops take more than 400 liters of water to produce one kilogram of product. Alfalfa hay, for example, commonly requires more than 1,000 liters of water for each kilogram of dry hay produced. In contrast, in nonirrigated farming only a small amount of water is used. A sheep will use about 6 liters of water each day, a horse about 40 liters of water a day. A cow uses only about 10 liters of water to produce one liter of milk. A laying hen uses between one half and one liter of water per day. Consequently, in areas where water is very expensive or scarce, livestock or poultry industries can be developed more economically than water consuming types of industries.

Although most large cities and irrigation projects use water from surface streams, the economic importance of subsurface water can hardly be emphasized too strongly. Subsurface water is more desirable than surface water for at least six reasons. (1) It is commonly free of pathogenic organisms and needs no purification for domestic or industrial uses. (2) The temperature is nearly constant, which is a great advantage if the water is used for heat exchange. (3) Turbidity and color are generally absent. (4) Chemical composition is commonly constant. (5) Ground-water storage is generally greater than surface-water storage, so that ground-water supplies are not seriously affected by short droughts. (6) Radiochemical and biological contamination of most ground water is difficult. Ground water, which has been stored by nature through many years of recharge, is available in many areas which do not have dependable surface water supplies.

Three common disadvantages discourage ground-water development in some areas. (1) Most important is the fact that many regions are underlain by rocks with insufficient porosity or permeability to yield much water to wells. (2) Usually, but not always, ground water has a greater dissolved solids content than surface water in the same region. (3) The cost of developing wells is commonly greater than the cost of developing small streams. This is particularly true in regions of moderate to high precipitation.

References

[1]Meinzer, O., *Hydrology*, p. 4, Dover, New York, 1942.

[2]Mead, D., *Hydrology, the Fundamental Basis of Hydraulic Engineering*, 1st Ed., McGraw-Hill, New York, 1919 (626 pp.); 2nd Ed., McGraw-Hill, New York, 1950 (717 pp.).

[3]Bowman, Isaiah, "Well-Drilling Methods," *U. S. Geographical Survey Water-Supply Paper* 257, pp. 23-30 (1911).

[4]Tolman, C. F., *Ground Water*, Chapter I, pp. 1-25, McGraw-Hill, New York, 1937.

[5]Krynine, P. D. "On the Antiquity of Sedimentation and Hydrology (with Some Moral Conclusions)," *Bulletin Geological Society of America*, Vol. 71, pp. 1721-1726 (1960).

[6]Mariotte, E., *Oeuvres de Mr. Mariotte*, 2 Vols. (701 pp.). Edited by P. Van der Aa, Leiden, 1717.

[7]Hagen, G., *Handbuch der Wasserbaukunst*, Vol. I, p. 87, Bornträger, Koenigsberg, 1853.

[8]Darcy, H., *Les fontaines publiques de la ville de Dijon*, V. Dalmont, Paris, 1856 (674 pp.).

[9]Sheppard, T., "William Smith, His Maps and Memoirs," *Proceedings Yorkshire Geological Society*, Vol. 19, new series, pp. 75-253 (1917).

[10]Daubrée, A., *Les eaux souterraines, aux époques anciennes et à l'époque actuelle*, Dunod, Paris, 3 Vols., 1887.

[11]Hackett, O. M., "The Father of Modern Ground-Water Hydrology," *Ground Water* (Journal of the NWWA), Vol. 2, pp. 2-5 (April 1964).

[12]Dupuit, J., *Etudes théoriques et pratiques sur le mouvement des eaux dans les canaux découverts et à travers les terrains perméables*, 2nd Ed., Dunod, Paris, 1863 (304 pp.).

[13]Thiem, A., *Hydrologische Methoden*, Gebhardt, Leipzig, 1906 (56 pp.).

[14]Forchheimer, Ph., *Uber die Ergebigkeit von Brunnen Anlagen und Sickerschlitzen*, Zeitschrift des Architekten und Ingenieur Vereins zu Hannover, Vol. 32, pp. 539-564 (1886).

[15]Slichter, C. S., "Theoretical Investigation of the Motion of Ground Water," U. S. Geological Survey, *19th Annual Report*, pp. 2, 295-384 (1889)

[16]Muskat, M., *The Flow of Homogeneous Fluids through Porous Media*, McGraw-Hill, New York, 1937 (763 pp.); Second Printing, J. W. Edwards, Ann Arbor, Michigan, 1946.

[17]Hubbert, M. King, "The Theory of Ground-Water Motion." *Journal of Geology*, November, December, 1940.

[18]Pavlovsky, N. N., *Collected Works*, 2 Vols., Akad. Nauk, USSR, Leningrad, 1956.

[19]De Wiest, R. J. M., "Translator's Remarks," *The Theory of Ground-Water Movement*, p. ix, Princeton University Press, Princeton, New Jersey, 1962. (Original work by P. Ya. Polubarinova-Kochina.)

[20]*Ibid.*

XVI

WHAT HAPPENS TO RAIN or melted snow when it sinks into the ground? Where does it go? The following selection by John G. Ferris discusses the characteristics of subsurface water and the natural laws that control the movements and storage of ground water.

Ground Water

OUR STUDY of the waters of the earth progresses from the more familiar fields of atmospheric water and surface water to the third province of hydrology, which deals with the study of subsurface or ground water. Among the many prerequisites necessary to the study of groundwater hydrology, probably the one most neglected in the training of engineers is the subject of geology. Inasmuch as it would be impossible to correct this deficiency in any single chapter, it is necessarily assumed that the student has sufficient background training in this field to recognize the degree to which geology controls the occurrence and movement of ground water.

Although man has long been familiar with the development of small water supplies from wells, it is only since the demands upon our ground water have become heavy that much thought has been directed to the hydraulics of ground-water flow. The great advances made since the turn of the century in the improvement of well-drilling methods and pumping equipment, particularly in the development of the deep-well turbine pump, have resulted in a marked upward trend in the use of ground water for domestic, rural, municipal, and industrial water supply. It is of interest to note that in 1939 it was estimated, that, in the United States, about 9100 public water supplies were derived from ground water and about 3300 from surface sources. Superimpose on this established upward trend the demands of industry awakened to the economic advantages of ground water for air temperature and humidity control and as a relatively constant quality source lending itself to almost fixed treatment. Notwithstanding the magnitude of the total withdrawal of ground water for all the above uses, this total is exceeded by the present demand for ground water in irrigation.

An ever-increasing number of problems has attended the rapid growth in the use of ground water. Those engaged in the search for answers to these problems are handicapped by the deficiencies in hydrologic research and the lack of trained technicians in this field. Our ground-water reserves have, too frequently, been called inexhaustible. Advances in hydrology show the fallacy of such a belief. Equally unfavorable, however, is the dissemination of discouraging opinions by those who have experienced water shortages that result from overdevelopment. It becomes increasingly evident that a wiser and fuller use of this great national resource can be achieved only by the sound and rational methods of the trained hydrogeologist and hydrogeological engineer.

The earth's crust, composed of its myriad and varied hard rocks and the unconsolidated overburden, serves as a vast underground reservoir for the storage and transmission of percolating ground waters. The rocks comprising the earth's crust are seldom if ever solid throughout. They contain numerous openings called interstices that vary through a wide range of sizes and shapes. Although these interstices may reach cavernous size in some rocks, it should be noted that most of them are very small. Generally, they are interconnected, permitting movement of the percolating waters, but in some rocks they are isolated, preventing the transmission of water between interstices. Accordingly, then, the mode of occurrence of ground water in the rocks of a given area is largely determined by the geology of that area.

Porosity

The physical property of a rock that defines the degree to which it contains interstices is termed its *porosity* and is expressed quantitatively as the percentage that the interstitial volume is of the total. The porosity of a material is dependent on the interrelation of size, shape, and manner of sorting of its component parts in unconsolidated or pervious sedimentary material; or on the size, shape, and pattern of channeling in relatively soluble rock such as limestone; or on the size, shape, and pattern of fracturing in the dense sedimentary, igneous, and metamorphic rocks. Some idea

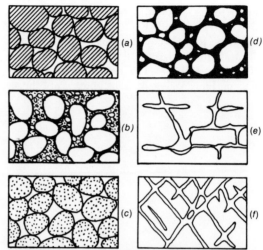

After Meinzer, *U. S. Geological Survey Water-Supply Paper,* 489, 1923, Fig. 1, p. 3

Figure 1 *Diagram showing several types of rock interstices and the relation of rock texture to porosity. a, Well-sorted sedimentary deposit having high porosity; b, poorly-sorted sedimentary deposit having low porosity; c, well-sorted sedimentary deposit consisting of pebbles that are themselves porous, so that the deposit as a whole has a very high porosity; d, well-sorted sedimentary deposit whose porosity has been diminished by the deposition of mineral matter in the interstices; e, rock rendered porous by solution; f, rock rendered porous by fracturing.*

of the relation of porosity to rock texture and particle sorting may be gained by reference to figure 1.

The porosity of rock or unconsolidated material may range from considerably less than 1 per cent to more than 50 per cent. However, a porosity in excess of 40 per cent is rare, except in soils or poorly compacted materials. In general, we may consider a porosity greater than 20 per cent as large, between 5 and 20 per cent as medium, and less than 5 per cent as small.

There are a number of methods in use for determining the porosity of rocks or soils which are based on either volumetric or specific-gravity measurements of dry versus saturated samples. The relation of the factors most commonly required for porosity tests is summarized by the following equation,[2]

$$p = 100\left(\frac{W}{V}\right) = 100\left(\frac{V - v}{V}\right) =$$

$$100\left(\frac{S - a}{S}\right) = 100(b - a)$$

where p is porosity, W volume of water required to saturate dry sample of rock or soil, V volume of sample, v aggregate volume of solid particles comprising the sample, S weighted average of specific gravities of minerals composing the soil or rock, a specific gravity of dry samples, and b specific gravity of saturated sample.

Rather elaborate core-sampling apparatus have been devised to obtain samples in an undisturbed condition. However, the removal of any sample from its original environment is certain to disturb the sample to some extent. There is no positive assurance that any laboratory procedure reproduces the original regimen of pressure, temperature, or volume. Furthermore, in the final analysis the sample represents only an infinitesimal section of the soil or rock formation.

Specific Yield

Another physical characteristic which is of importance in the hydrology of ground water is the *specific yield*. When saturated rocks or soils are drained under the action of gravity, it is found that the volume of water yielded by draining is less than the volume of void space indicated by the total porosity of the material because of the pellicular water that is retained by molecular attraction. The quantity of water yielded by gravity drainage from saturated water-bearing material is termed the specific yield and is expressed as a percentage of the total volume of the material drained. The quantity of water retained by the ma-

terial against the pull of gravity is termed the *specific retention* or *field capacity* and is again expressed as a percentage of the total volume of the material. A somewhat similar term, moisture equivalent,[3] is frequently used to represent the moisture retained by a saturated sample when subjected to an arbitrary centrifugal force. It is evident that the sum of the specific yield and the specific retention of a material is equal to its porosity.

If evaporation is prevented, the greater part of the water retained by a column of rock or sand and gravel, after draining for 24 hours, will be retained almost indefinitely as a film by molecular adhesion on the walls of the interstices. The greater the amount of total interstitial surface in a rock or unconsolidated material the greater is its specific retention. As would be expected, it is found that, as the effective diameter of grain decreases, the specific retention generally increases because the total exposed surface area increases with decreasing grain size.

Although the total porosity of a clay or fine sand might be equivalent to the total porosity of a coarse gravel, it follows from the foregoing statements that the large specific retention of the clay would result in a very small specific yield, whereas the reverse would be true for the coarse gravel. For practical purposes, a water-bearing formation of coarse gravel would supply large quantities of water to wells, whereas clay formations, although saturated and of high porosity, would be of little value in this respect. Accordingly, we find that specific yield is termed by some as the effective or practical porosity.

Determinations of the specific yield or specific retention by laboratory methods are limited by the difficulties of securing undisturbed and representative samples that are noted under permeability determinations by laboratory methods. In addition, the short sample columns used in the laboratory cannot duplicate the very long capillary tubes that probably exist in the thick sections found in the field. As for permeability, the most satisfactory determinations of specific yield are made in the field through the medium of pumping tests.

Permeability and Transmissibility

The vertical percolation of ground water through capillary interstices results in the build-up of a hydraulic gradient with consequent lateral percolation of water through interconnecting interstices. The capacity of a formation for transmitting water is measured by its *coefficient of permeability*, which is defined by Meinzer[4] as the rate of flow of water in gallons per day through a cross-sectional area of 1 square foot under a hydraulic gradient of 1 foot per foot at a temperature of 60° F.

The term *coefficient of transmissibility* introduced by Theis[5] is coming into popular usage in ground-water hydrology. The coefficient of transmissibility is defined as the rate of flow of water in gallons per day through a vertical strip of the aquifer 1 foot wide and extending the full saturated height under a hydraulic gradient of 100 per cent at a temperature of 60° F. The difference between the coefficients of permeability and transmissibility is shown in diagrammatic form by figure 2.

The permeability of granular material varies with the diameter and degree of assortment of the individual particles. A well-sorted gravel has a much higher permeability than a well-sorted coarse sand. However, gravel with a moderate percentage of medium- and fine-grained material may be considerably less permeable than a uniformly sized coarse sand. In graded material, the particles of moderate size fill the pore spaces between the larger particles, and in turn the resultant pore spaces are filled by the fine materials, thus forming

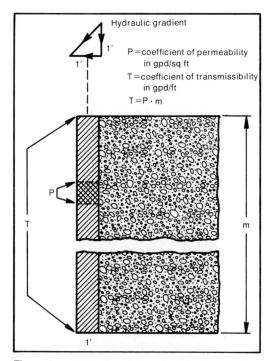

Figure 2

a compactly knit and impervious mass such as is obtained in good concrete.

Measurements of the permeability of rocks and unconsolidated materials may be made by either field or laboratory methods as described by Muskat[6] and by Wenzel[7]. Laboratory determinations of the coefficient of permeability are made by measuring the discharge or the time rate of change in head, for the percolation of measured quantities of water through a known area and volume of soil sample. Devices used for this purpose are termed *permeameters* and include a supply reservoir or tank from which water is discharged through a percolation cylinder under either a constant or a variable head. The percolation cylinder is accurately machined to a fixed diameter and is equipped with a base screen which supports the soil sample and permits free inflow of water. Manometer tubes in the supply and receiving reservoirs are used to determine the loss of head that occurs for the vertical percolation of known quantities of water through the soil cylinder at measured rates. A schematic representation of the more common types of permeameter is shown in figure 3.

The use of permeameters to determine the permeability of unconsolidated material is invalidated to a large degree because of the great errors introduced in repacking a disturbed sample. Inasmuch as the packing arrangement is a critical factor in determining the permeability of an incoherent material, it would seem advisable to apply laboratory methods only to consolidated materials or cores of unconsolidated material. Further caution should be exercised because the volume of material used in permeameter tests represents only an infinitesimal sample of a formation that is generally quite heterogeneous. Accordingly, to be of value permeameter programs should include many samples collected at frequent depth intervals and at numerous locations within the area.

Field determinations of permeability are made by either the velocity or the potential method. In the velocity method one well is used for the injection of salt, dye, or an electrolyte. Two or more wells are used as observation stations to determine the time rate of travel of the injected substance through the water-bearing material. Fluorescein is generally used for the dye method and can be detected by eye or in more dilute form by colorimeter. The chemical or salt method requires periodic sampling and analysis of water from each observation well to determine the time of arrival of the salted solution. The electrolyte method requires periodic readings of the electric conductivity of the water in each observation well. Measurements of the water-table gradient, the distance between observation wells, and the time of travel of the injected material provide the basis for determining the permeability of the material over the path of travel. A sketch of the equipment setup for one form of the velocity method is shown in figure 4.

Inasmuch as the velocity of flow through

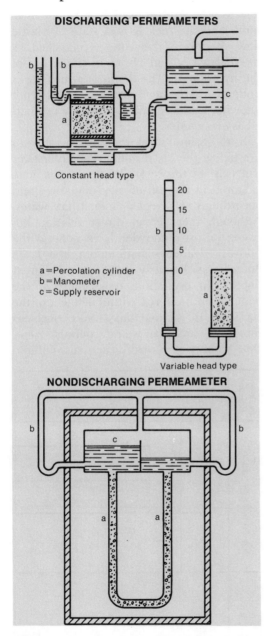

DISCHARGING PERMEAMETERS

Constant head type

a = Percolation cylinder
b = Manometer
c = Supply reservoir

Variable head type

NONDISCHARGING PERMEAMETER

Figure 3

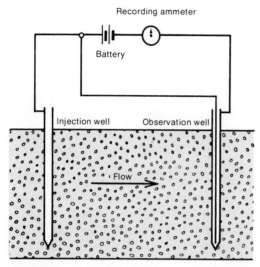

Figure 4

most ground-water aquifers is measured in terms of a few feet per day, it is necessary that velocity observations be confined to small areas in order to secure results within a reasonable time. This method measures the velocity of the fastest thread of water that happens to intersect the two wells and not necessarily the average velocity between the wells. This method would be impractical for sampling adequately any heterogeneous aquifer that has large variations in vertical and horizontal permeability.

Potential methods of determining permeability are based on measurements of the amount and rate of drawdown or recovery of water level in observation wells at different distances from a well that is either pumping or recovering from pumping, respectively. . . . A distinct advantage of the potential method is its ability to sample large areas of the undistrubed aquifer within a limited time and at a minimum of expense.

The Ground-Water Reservoir

The classification of the earth's crust with reference to its properties as a reservoir for the storage and transmission of percolating ground waters and the subdivision of this reservoir into its component parts is shown in figure 5. Interstices are probably absent in the zone of rock flowage, because the stresses are beyond the elastic limit, and the rock is in a state of plastic flow. Water in this zone is classified as internal water and is not in the realm of the hydrologist. The depth at which rocks undergo permanent deformation is not known accurately but is generally estimated as many miles.

In the zone of rock fracture, the stresses are below the elastic limit, and interstices can exist in the rocks. Water in this zone is stored in the soil of rock interstices and accordingly is termed interstitial water. Although there is no direct relation between porosity and depth, in general the porosity decreases with depth, the large openings particularly being absent at great depths. In crystalline rocks most of the water is encountered within 300 feet of the surface.[8] In sedimentary rocks, such as limestone and sandstone, porous zones that yield water readily are encountered

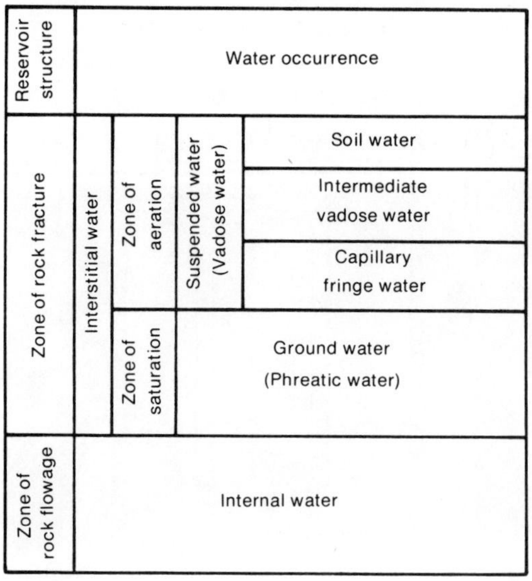

Reservoir structure			Water occurrence		
Zone of rock fracture	Interstitial water	Zone of aeration	Suspended water (Vadose water)	Soil water
				Intermediate vadose water
				Capillary fringe water
		Zone of saturation	Ground water (Phreatic water)	
Zone of rock flowage			Internal water	

Figure 5

in some places at depths of more than 6000 feet, although most wells in these strata find little water below a depth of 2000 feet. The decrease in size of interstices with increased depth is caused in part by the increased pressure at great depth, which tends to close the pore spaces or crevices, and in part by the cementation of interstices by the heavier and more highly mineralized waters.

The zone of aeration is that part of the earth's crust where the water present is not under hydrostatic pressure, except temporarily, and for the most part the interstices are filled with atmospheric gases. Water retained in this zone is held by molecular attraction and is termed pellicular, suspended, or vadose water. The thickness of the zone of aeration varies considerably depending on the geology, hydrology, and topography of the area. It may be virtually nonexistent in lowland areas adjacent to bodies of surface water as in marsh lands, or it may be as much as 1000 feet thick as in arid regions of great topographic relief.

The belt of soil water consists of the soil and other unconsolidated materials in which the root systems of plants, grasses, and trees are developed and from which water is discharged to the atmosphere by evaporation or transpiration. Evaporation occurs largely at the surface, except in tight clay soils under prolonged drying, where shrinkage cracks develop and permit air circulation to some depth. Although water may be brought to the evaporation areas by capillarity, in general water is not discharged in appreciable quantities by evaporation below depths of a few feet. As to transpiration, note that, although the root penetration of most common grasses and field crops is seldom more than a few feet, records indicate root development for wheat to depths of 7 feet, for alfalfa as much as 30 feet, and for some per-

ennials in arid regions as much as 50 feet.

The capillary fringe is the belt overlying the zone of saturation and containing interstices, some or all of which are filled with water that is in connection with and is a continuation of the zone of saturation, being held above that zone by capillarity acting against the force of gravity. The thickness of the capillary fringe in granular material is a function of the effective particle size and generally increases as the grain size decreases. The fringe thickness may range from a few inches in coarse gravel to 8 feet in silty material and is probably much greater in very fine-grained sediments. The capillary fringe in a given material may vary slightly in thickness from summer to winter because of changes in water temperature. The surface tension of water increases as the temperature decreases, and within the range of 60° to 32° F it increases about 3 per cent. Although the density of water varies with temperature, this change is negligible. Accordingly, then, the thickness of the capillary fringe would be somewhat greater in late winter and spring, the period of lowered groundwater temperature.

Beneath the capillary fringe lies the zone of saturation. It is this zone that is of importance to the hydraulic engineer and well driller as the source of water for wells and springs. It is of importance to the hydrologic cycle by serving as the mechanism for the intake, transport, and return of underground waters and to the surface and the atmosphere. The upper surface of the zone of saturation is called the *water table*.

Water Table and Artesian Aquifers

Although idealized conditions are found frequently in the field, usually an actual cross section of a valley is more complex. Field reconnaissance may reveal more than one water-bearing formation with considerable variation in the character of each stratum. The many geologic processes involved, coupled with the great variations in intensity and duration of the forces in action during each stage of development leading up to the existing structures, have resulted in an infinite number of variations in the geologic and hydrologic dimensions of the ground-water reservoir. The "hodge-podge" assortment of the drift cover in glaciated areas typifies these complexities. However, the heterogeneous nature of the surficial materials does not invalidate the fundamental principles but merely complicates their application.

A stratum or formation of permeable material that will yield gravity ground water in appreciable quantities is termed an *aquifer*. The term "appreciable quantity" is relative because, where ground water is obtained with difficulty, even fine-grained, poorly productive materials may be classed as principal aquifers. If an aquifer is over-lain by a confining bed of impervious material and if the water level in a tightly cased well penetrating the aquifer rises above the bottom of the confining bed, the aquifer is termed *artesian*. The over-lying confining bed is an *aquiclude*. The artesian aquifer differs from the water-table aquifer in that the surface, formed by contouring or connecting the heights of the water level in tightly cased wells tapping the aquifer, is not a free surface exposed to the soil atmosphere but is an imaginary pressure surface standing above the body of the aquifer. Consequently it receives the name of piezometric surface. Although the term piezometric surface can be applied also to the water-table surface, the reverse is not true. Contours drawn on the piezo-metric surface are referred to as isopiestic lines. A diagrammatic cross section illus-trating the application of the above termi-nology is shown in figure 6.

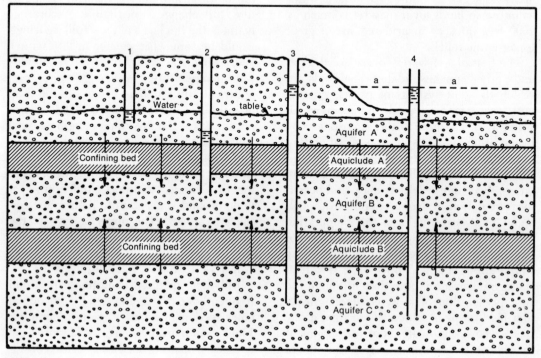

Figure 6

The water level in well 1, which taps aquifer *A*, coincides with the water table or surface of the zone of saturation in this aquifer, and consequently well 1 is a non-artesian or water-table well. The water levels in wells 2, 3, and 4 stand above the base of the overlying aquiclude, and aquifers *B* and *C* are artesian. Region *a-a* is an area of artesian flow, and well 4 is a flowing well. The lower static level in aquifer *B* indicates that water is moving from aquifer *A* or *C* into aquifer *B* through a distant break in aquiclude *A* or *B* or by vertical leakage through the aquicludes. The high head in wells 3 and 4 indicates that the recharge or intake area of aquifer *C* is at a relatively high elevation, probably above the land surface shown in the cross section. Aquifers like *B* and *C*, which contain confined ground water, are pressure conduits and exhibit interesting elastic phenomena.

Elastic Properties of Artesian Aquifers

It is a common observation that wells in some areas will undergo changes of water level during periods of large fluctuation in barometric pressure. A representation of the mechanism causing the change of water level under varying air pressure and a hydrograph from a well exhibiting this effect are shown in figure 7. As the barometric pressure increases, the water level in the well casing tends to be depressed. An equal effect is exerted on the soil column and on the shallow water table with a resultant balance of the pressure inside and outside the well tapping the shallow aquifer, and consequently no net change in water level occurs. In the deeper aquifer, however, the overlying aquiclude is competent to some degree in resisting the load imposed by the rising barometer

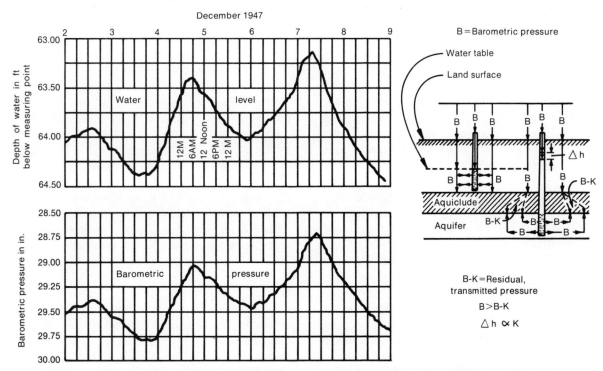

Figure 7 *Idealized cross-section of aquifer showing how bridging action of overlying aquiclude sets up pressure differential in the underlying aquifer which is balanced by a change in hydrostatic head.*

and does not transmit the full effect of the air pressure change. Consequently, the water level in the well tapping confined ground water is depressed an amount equal to the proportion of the barometric pressure change that is not transmitted by the aquiclude. The ratio of water-level change to the barometric change, in equivalent units, is termed the barometric efficiency of the well. Note that the effect is inverse, that is, as the barometric pressure rises the water level declines.

Inasmuch as the increased hydrostatic pressure in the aquifer, which accompanies a rise in barometric pressure, exceeds the residual pressure transmitted through the aquiclude, a net positive pressure is exerted on the aquiclude. As a result of this pressure, the aquiclude is compressed slightly, or, conversely, the aquifer expands a small amount. The slight increase in aquifer volume accommodates the water displaced from the well casing by the increased pressure on the water surface. Changes in barometric pressure are generally of very short duration compared to the time required for the displaced water to move through the formation for any distance. Consequently, barometric fluctuations are recorded in confined aquifers if the overlying aquiclude is competent to resist pressure and extends over an appreciable area. Wells located near an outcrop area or near a break in the aquiclude, where contact with the surface or surface formations occurs within close proximity to the well, will not exhibit barometric effects.

Reports of blowing and sucking wells which exhibit pronounced updraft or downdraft of air at the well mouth may be explained by the barometric effects noted above. These reports are especially prevalent where an extensive aquiclude occurs some distance above the water table, so that there is a body of air confined between the water table and the aquiclude, which communicates with the atmosphere only through wells. Also the frequent reference to noticeable cloudiness or color in the well water preceding a storm might be explained in part by the rapid rise of water level, which would accompany a barometric low and would bring into the well silty or fine material, as a result of the quick inrush of water through the screen. Some cloudiness may also be caused by gas that escapes from solution when the atmospheric pressure is lowered.

Superimposed loads on the earth's crust also produce changes of water level in wells tapping confined ground water, as indicated in figure 8, which shows an autographic record of water-level fluctuation caused by railroad trains passing within 100 feet of the observation well. The alternate loading and unloading of the earth's crust by ocean tides in the coastal areas results in a corresponding cycle of water-level fluctuation in wells as shown in figure 9. In these cases, the resultant of the impressed pressure that is transmitted to the aquifer, because of the incompetency of the aquiclude to resist entirely the increase in pressure, causes a rise in water level in the well casing, and the ratio of this rise to the total load impressed is termed the tidal efficiency of the aquifer. Inasmuch as the tidal efficiency is a measure of the incompetency of the aquiclude and the barometric efficiency is a measure of its competency, it is evident that the sum of the barometric and tidal efficiencies of an aquifer must equal unity, as demonstrated mathematically by Jacob.[9]

Subsurface Leakage

The presence of aquicludes or confining layers of considerable thickness and of dense, compact texture has probably served to further the somewhat popular but quite erroneous belief that the artesian aquifers are insulated strata containing connate

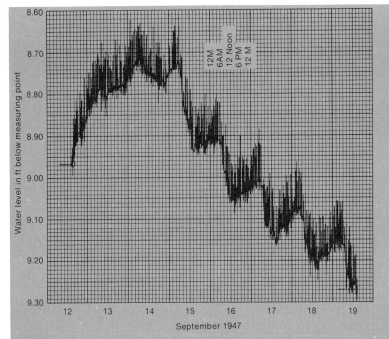

Figure 8 *Hydrograph from automatic water-stage recorder in operation on well tapping Marshall sandstone at Battle Creek, Michigan. Short-period vertical displacements superimposed on curve are water-level fluctuations caused by artesian loading from passing railroad trains.*

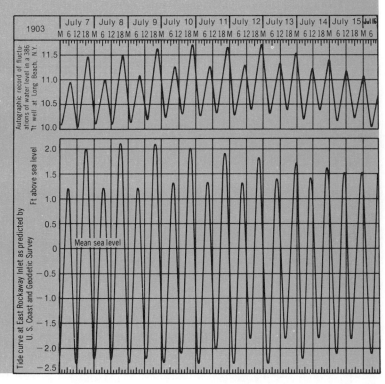

Figure 9 *Hydrograph showing fluctuations of water level in a 386-ft. well at Long Beach, N. Y., as compared to the tide at East Rockaway Inlet, N. Y.*

waters. In this connection, it should be noted that many of our highly developed artesian aquifers would be dry today if such insulation were general. Fortunately, however, most aquifers receive recharge either through direct infiltration on outcrop areas, through permeable breaks in the confining aquicludes, or by means of leakage through the aquiclude itself. Like many physical terms, the word impervious is only relative and not absolute because air or water will permeate most materials if sufficient time and pressure are involved.

To demonstrate the possible magnitude of aquiclude leakage, there is represented in figure 10 an idealized cross section of a geologic condition that is found frequently in the field. It is assumed that the average coefficient of permeability is 2000 gallons per day per square foot for aquifer B and 0.2 gallons per day per square foot for aquiclude A, or a ratio of 10,000 to 1. The permeability value selected for the aquifer is representative of the average obtained for many sand and gravel formations. The value selected for the aquiclude corresponds to a sample of clayey silt tested in the hydrologic laboratory of the U. S. Geo-

logical Survey. The mechanical analysis for this material indicates clay, 49.3 per cent, silt, 45.3 per cent, and material larger than silt but less than 0.50 mm, 5.4 per cent; the porosity was 55.5 per cent. Assume that the water table in the shallow aquifer has a head 50 feet greater than the piezometric surface in the deeper aquifer. Assign a thickness of 50 feet for aquiclude A. With the foregoing conditions, it is calculated that the leakage through the aquiclude from the shallow to the deep aquifer would occur at the rate of 0.2 gallons per day per square foot of aquiclude area. This seems a minor item at first consideration, but for each square mile the leakage totals 5.6 million gallons per day, or enough to supply a community of 56,000 people at an average rate of 100 gallons per capita per day. When we consider the many square miles of contributing area available to most large aquifers, it is evident that the assumed aquiclude can contain even less pervious material and still pass appreciable quantities of water.

For the assumed conditions with a porosity of 56 percent, the movement of water through the aquiclude would occur at the rate of 0.6 inches per day or require about 3 years for a traverse through the 50 foot section. Accordingly, then, an aquifer recharged only by leakage from adjacent aquicludes will not show water-level fluctuations in response to short period changes in precipitation rate.

In addition to the dewatering problems in subsurface construction where aquifers are exposed by excavation, other difficult problems may arise in deep excavation into an overlying aquiclude. Prior to excavation, the stresses in an aquiclude would be in equilibrium with the total force exerted by the underlying aquifer. Assume that at the site the aquifer has a large hydrostatic head and a high transmissibility. The aquiclude over a long period of time has com-

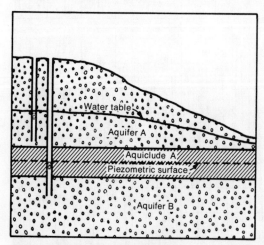

Figure 10 *Generalized cross-section of shallow and deep aquifer showing differential hydrostatic head.*

pacted to a thickness that provides the inherent stability to balance the upward pressure from the aquifer. Although detailed information is not available, it would seem probable that any excavation to appreciable depth in the aquiclude might disturb the force balance to an extent that might result in upheaval of the pit floor and general instability. If rupture of the aquiclude occurred or if permeable zones were exposed, large boils or springs might develop. A condition of this type might be remedied by a few properly spaced wells that penetrate the deep aquifer and are pumped at a rate sufficient to reduce the pressure and restore an equilibrium state.

Underflow

To all who are acquainted with the construction of blind drains, the type of ground-water flow termed underflow will strike a familiar chord. The geologic "horse" in sedimentary rock and the buried kames, eskers, alluvium, and outwash channels in the drift mantle are examples of nature's large-scale underdrains. Underflow may occur under either water-table or artesian conditions as shown in figure 11. Inasmuch as the word channel is generally used in surface-water terminology for flow with a free surface, the term underflow channel can be assigned for the water-table condition because a free surface exists. In a similar manner, underflow conduit can be used for the artesian condition because the term conduit generally implies confined flow.

In periods of extended drought many stream channels, though dry with reference to surface flow, may carry appreciable quantities of water as underflow. In view of the vast network of preglacial and interglacial stream channels throughout the glaciated areas of the United States, plus the evidence that many of these buried channels are very large, it becomes evident

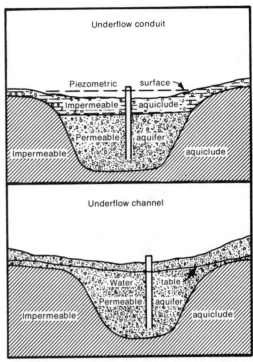

Figure 11

that the underflow in channels filled with very permeable material may be an appreciable part of the base flow from some drainage basins. Although the velocity of such underflow would be very much less than surface flow, the total discharge becomes appreciable if large areas are involved.

Seepage

The movement of water between ground-water aquifers and surface sources is termed seepage. It is further classified as influent seepage, which is recharge from surface bodies of water, and effluent seepage, which is discharge to surface bodies of water. Thus surface streams are influent streams if the stream contributes water to the ground-water reservoir and effluent streams if water is received from the water table. A sketch of conditions existing in each type is shown in figure 12. The local

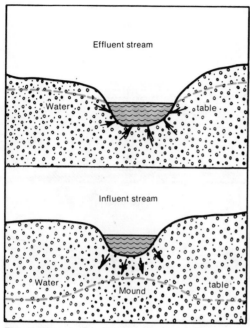

Figure 12

build-up of head on the water table under-lying an influent stream is termed a ground-water mound. The so-called base flow of surface streams is the effluent seepage from the drainage basin. During periods of pro-longed drought, when the total flow of a stream is restricted to the base flow, the stream is functioning solely as a drain. Accordingly, the collection of pertinent data concerning the volume of discharge and the time rate of water-table decline for base-flow periods, which is one phase of present field investigations conducted by the U. S. Geological Survey, will provide in time the basis for application of drain formulas and the ultimate forecast of base flow for major streams.

References

[1] "Inventory of Water Supply Facilities," *Eng. News-Record*, 1939, vol. 123, p. 414.

[2] O. E. Meinzer, "The Occurrence of Ground Water in the United States," *U. S. Geol. Survey Water-Supply Paper* 489, 1923, p. 12.

[3] L. J. Briggs and J. W. McLane, "The Moisture Equivalent of Soils," *U. S. Dept. Agr. Bur. of Soils Bull.* 45, 1907.

[4] N. D. Stearns, "Laboratory Tests on Physical Properties of Water-Bearing Materials," *U. S. Geol. Survey Water-Supply Paper* 596, 1927, p. 148.

[5] C. V. Theis, "The Relation between the Lower-ing of the Piezometric Surface and the Rate and Duration of Discharge of a Well Using Ground Water Storage," *Trans. Am. Geophys. Union*, 1935, p. 520.

[6] Morris Muskat, *Flow of Homogeneous Fluids through Porous Media*, McGraw-Hill, 1937. L K. Wenzel and V. C. Fishel, "Methods for Determining Permeability of Water-Bearing Materials," *U. S. Geol. Survey Water-Supply Paper* 887, 1942.

[8] E. E. Ellis, "Occurrence of Water in Crystalline Rocks," *U. S. Geol. Survey Water-Supply Paper* 160, 1906, pp. 19-28.

[9] C. E. Jacob, "On the Flow of Water in an Elastic Artesian Aquifer," *Trans. Am. Geophys. Union*, 1940, p. 583.

XVII

THE DESERTS OF THE WORLD are many and varied. The process of their formation still remains a mystery to geologists. One of the primary characteristics of all deserts is drought, which leads to the common misconception that water in any form is sorely lacking in such regions. William C. Putnam explodes this myth and shows how most of the landforms in deserts appear to have been shaped by running water.

Deserts

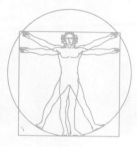

I

LEAST familiar of land areas, aside from the extreme arctic, are the world's deserts. Perhaps their seeming mystery lies in their relative remoteness from lands such as western Europe and the Atlantic coast of North America, where the modern pattern of western civilization developed. Had western life remained centered on the Mediterranean, deserts would be much closer to our daily lives because the limitations imposed by aridity bear heavily on such bordering countries as Spain, Morocco, Algeria, Libya, Egypt, and Israel. In earlier days much of the southern shore of the Mediterranean was the granary of Rome, and once-flourishing cities, such as Leptus Magnus in Libya, are now stark ruins half buried in the sand. One of the problems in studying deserts is that the boundaries are not fixed inexorably, but may expand or contract through the centuries. In fact, there is much evidence from paleobotany—the study of fossil plants—that deserts are relatively late arrivals among the Earth's landscapes. Deserts require a rather specialized set of circumstances for their existence, and in a moment we shall inquire into what some of these are.

First of all we need a working agreement as to what constitutes a desert. Temperature is not the only factor; some are hot almost all the time, others may have hot summers and cold winters, and some are cold throughout much of the year. Since drought is their common factor, in a general way we might call those regions deserts where more water would evaporate than actually falls as rain. In other words, the criterion we are using is relative rather than absolute, such as saying all regions are deserts that have less than 10 inches of rainfall in a year.

Drought is their prevailing characteristic, and deserts notably are regions of sparse vegetation. Few are completely devoid of plants, but some come very close to this ultimate limit. Typically, desert plants are widely spaced. Their colors tend to be subdued and drab, blending with their surroundings. Their leaves may

Courtesy of Trans World Airlines

Figure 1 *The desert crowds the edge of the irrigated flood plain of the Nile near Giza, Egypt.*

be small and leathery in order to reduce evaporation. In fact, some, as the *saguaro* of Arizona or the barrel cactus of the Sonoran Desert, may have no leaves at all. Other desert plants, such as the ubiquitous sage, may develop an extraordinarily deep root system in proportion to the part of the plant that shows above ground. Plants with these adaptations of extensive roots, leathery leaves, and large water-holding capacity are called *xerophytes*, from a combination of Greek words meaning dry + plant.

Every gradation exists in deserts, from those that are completely arid and that are essentially barren expanses of rock and sand, devoid of almost all visible plants, to deserts which support a nearly continuous cover of such plants as sagebrush and short grass. Dry regions with such a characteristic seasonal cover are best referred to as *steppe*, and commonly are marginal to the more desolate wastes.

The accompanying map of the world (figure 2) shows that the dry regions are concentrated in subtropical and in middle latitude parts of the Earth's surface. For example, there is nearly continuous desert from Cape Verde on the west coast of Africa, across the Sahara, the barren interior of Arabia, the desolate mountains of

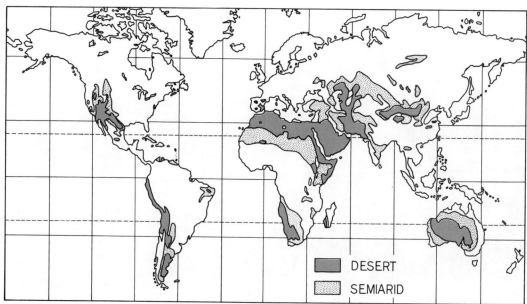

From P. Meigs, in *Future of Arid Lands*, AAAS Pub. No. 43, 1956. Copyright 1956 by the American Association for the Advancement of Science.

Figure 2 *Dry regions are found chiefly in the subtropics and the middle latitudes. They occur (1) below the high pressure cells in the atmosphere where descending air is being heated, (2) along cold-water coasts where moisture-laden air (fog) is transported to the warmer land, and (3) to the lee of high mountain ranges where descending air is being warmed.*

southern Iran, and on to the banks of the Indus in Pakistan. All told, 18 or 19 million square miles, or 36 per cent of the land surface of the Earth, might be classed as arid.

This statement brings us to the problem of definitions once more. Many regions marginal to the tropics and having a monsoonal climate are arid and drought burdened during the dry season, yet are rain sodden and soaked during the wet season. In the dry season many trees shed their leaves, thorn-bearing plants with woody, unyielding branches are a genuine obstacle to travel, and the ground is baked and sun-dried to the point where agriculture is impossible.

Another region of deficient precipitation that is difficult to classify is the barren land of the Arctic. The precipitation may be 10 inches a year or less, yet with a low evaporation rate, the tundra appears to be far better watered than it is. This illusion is aided by permafrost which keeps surface water from sinking very deep into the ground.

These cold deserts are so unlike the more typical dry lands of middle and low latitudes that we shall leave them out of this chapter in order to concentrate on the familiar sort of desert. The map (figure 2) shows that the preponderance of the dry areas of the Earth—exclusive of the Arctic—are on either side of the equator, chiefly around latitude 30°, and that they tend to favor the western side of continents.

Contrary to the popular image, most deserts are not vast shimmering seas of sand across which such picturesque characters as Foreign Legionnaires slog along while sheiks on spirited stallions sweep by. Although many deserts are sand covered, the majority are not. Most desert regions are more likely to be broad expanses of barren rock, or of stony ground with only a rudimentary soil profile developed. Ground colors are largely those of the original bedrock. They lack the red colors of tropical soils, especially those that are alternately wetted and dried, or the blacks and dark grays of humid temperate regions where the organic content in soil may be high. The bright red color that we associate with such places as Grand Canyon and Monument Valley comes in large part from coloring matter within the rocks themselves, rather than from red-soil forming processes active there today.

It is typical of many desert regions, especially those in continental interiors, that streams originating within the desert often falter and die within the desert's boundaries. This pattern of streams that do not reach the sea is called *interior drainage*, and is an unusual feature to a visitor from a well-watered region with through-flowing streams. Some desert streams simply wither away and sink into the sand. Others may carry enough water to maintain a lake at the end of their course. Since this will be a lake without an outlet, it is almost universally salty or brackish—the Dead Sea, about 1,300 feet below sea level at the end of the River Jordan, is a renowned example. A larger water body without an outlet is the Caspian Sea, covering about 164,000 square miles, and even though it is supplied by such a mighty river as the Volga, not enough water reaches it to overcome the inexorable losses of evaporation and to allow the lake to spill over the low divide separating it from the Don River and the Black Sea.

At many arid parts of the world, where the water brought in by streams cannot hold its own against evaporation, desert lakes may be only short-lived seasonal affairs, or may be completely dry for dec-

ades. Such ephemeral lakes, so characteristic of drought-burdened lands, are called *playas* in the southwestern United States. This is an extension of the meaning of the original Spanish word for beach or sandy bank of a river. Some playas may be glaring expanses of shimmering salt, such as the Bonneville Salt Flats near Great Salt Lake in Utah, or they may be broad, dead flat, clay-floored dry lakes—seemingly created for landing fields, they have such an ideally level surface.

Causes of Deserts

Before we launch into a discussion of the landforms in deserts and the nature of processes that operate there, it might be well to consider briefly what some of the special circumstances are that are responsible for causing some parts of the Earth's surface to be deprived of normal rainfall. Omitting the polar regions of deficient precipitation, there are three major types of arid regions. These are: (1) subtropical deserts, (2) deserts produced by cold coastal currents in tropical and subtropical regions, and (3) rain-shadow deserts.

The broad band of drought reaching across Africa and into India belongs in the first category, as do other similar dry subtropical lands. In part these deserts owe their existence to the presence of persistent high pressure cells in the atmosphere on both sides of the equator and centered approximately on the Tropic of Cancer and the Tropic of Capricorn. Since these cells are centers of descending, and therefore heating and drying air, land areas beneath them are burdened by persistent drought and exceptionally high evaporation rates. Years may pass between rains in such a desert as the interior of Arabia. Infrequent rains, when they do occur in these tropical deserts, may be violent and commonly result from a weakening of the pattern of high pressure and a resulting invasion of moisture bearing maritime-tropical or equatorial air.

In other parts of the tropics, dry lands are caused by the planetary air circulation toward the equator. This nearly constant current of air, better established over sea than land (where local differences of temperature may be pronounced), is given the old name of the *trade winds*. These winds were a boon to the masters of sailing ships of a century ago because they could be relied upon to blow almost constantly with about the same force and from the same direction. They blow in both the Northern and Southern Hemispheres toward the equatorial belt of calms. Because of the Earth's rotation these streams of air are deflected to the right in the Northern Hemisphere (looking in the direction the current flows), as other moving things such as ocean currents, or projectiles, or missiles are, too. This means that instead of blowing from due north or due south, at right angles to the equator, these winds come from the northeast, north of the equator, and from the southeast, south of it.

The trade winds, or others like them, blowing across land are drying winds because they are blowing from colder to warmer regions. The ability of air to hold water increases with temperature; it decreases as the temperature drops. As a current of air is forced to climb a mountain front which lies athwart its path, it is chilled and rain falls. This is strikingly shown by the high islands in the trade wind seas. Windward slopes, as in Hawaii, may receive 450 inches of rain (in one instance, 600 inches), while leeward slopes may have as little as 10 inches fall in a year.

Deserts formed because of cool coastal currents are perhaps the least familiar type to Americans. Such deserts flourish along the middle latitude coasts of continents whose shores are bathed by cold coastal currents, such as the Humboldt Current

off the Atacama Desert of Chile and Peru, or the Benguela Current off the Kalahari Desert of southwest Africa.

These deserts are exceptionally impressive for the very dramatic climatic contrasts encountered within extremely short distances. The Atacama Desert, for example, is among the drier lands on Earth, yet its seaward margin is concealed in a virtually unbroken gray wall of fog. Winds blowing across the cold waters of the coastal current are chilled, their moisture condenses and thus a seemingly eternal blanket of fog stands over the sea. Once this fog drifts landward to where the air temperature is higher, the fog burns off almost immediately, and the water-holding capacity of the air current increases rather than decreases as it moves across the heated land. A high, thin cover of fog may build up once more high on the Andean slopes, with the result that Lima, for example, is a sober, austere-looking city with a thin, unbroken pall of gray high-altitude fog spreading above it. The sun rarely shines, yet rain is equally rare, averaging perhaps 2 inches a year.

A third cause of aridity is the interposition of a mountain barrier in the path of a moisture-bearing air current. We have a striking example in western North America with the desert stretching eastward in the so-called rain shadow of the Sierra Nevada of California. The profile (figure 3) across this part of central California at the latitude of San Francisco shows the great disparity between precipitation on the western slope of the Sierra Nevada and the floor of the Nevada desert.

Few deserts are the product of a single cause operating to the exclusion of all others. The high deserts of Asia do not fit into the categories outlined above. They could scarcely be more remote from coastal currents, hot or cold, and they lie well outside the subtropical high pressure belt.

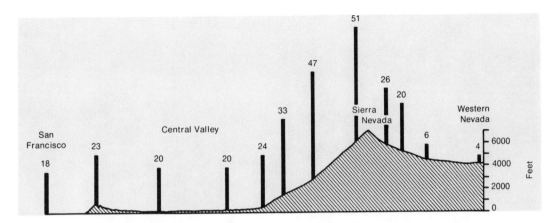

Figure 3 *Total rainfall at stations from coastal California across the Sierra Nevada to western Nevada, showing the effect of the mountain barrier in reducing precipitation to leeward.*

The factors entering into their origin certainly involve the enclosing ring of mountains, the great distance this so-called roof of the world lies from the sea—the ultimate source of water to be precipitated—and the northern location of this desert land which places it climatically in a part of the Earth where the barometric pressure is relatively high, and where cool, drying air descends from the higher levels of the atmosphere. This last reason also applies to many of the subtropical deserts.

In summary, we can say that deserts do not have a simple reason for their existence. Their origins are complex, but they are well worth trying to understand, not only for their own sake as an intellectual challenge but also because so much of the future of mankind is dependent upon the utilization of arid lands. An equally intriguing question is whether the boundaries of deserts are stationary, or whether they are contracting or expanding. The climate of the world has slowly changed in historic time. This is strikingly true of deserts, and much of the most compelling evidence comes from the Sahara and the Middle East (figures 4 and 5). Artifacts, stone implements, and rock paintings of extraordinary subtlety and sophistication testify to the presence

Figure 4 *Prehistoric rock paintings indicate that grazing animals once lived in the Sahara Desert.*

Figure 5 *Ruins of Roman baths, recently excavated in the North African desert, mark the site of a once-flourishing city.*

of early man in what are desolate expanses of the Sahara today. At a later date much of this barren region was the granary of Rome, and colonial cities of that day as well as roads along which the legions marched are now overrun by drifting sand. The expansion of the desert broke the slender thread of communication lines linking the cultures of the Mediterranean and African worlds. Apparently thereafter the two had a vague and uncertain awareness of each other over the centuries, but it was not until the introduction of the camel caravan that the land connection was re-established. By this time each culture had evolved along a different path.

Stream Erosion in an Arid Region

What are some of the things, other than drought, that set the deserts of the world apart from more favored lands? Paradoxical as it may seem the leading agency responsible for sculpturing the landforms of a desert is running water, just as it is in humid regions. Puzzling indeed is how all the work was done of removing the enormous volumes of rock that once filled the canyons of desert mountains, or of shaping the mountains themselves, or even of wearing them away completely to bare rock plains stretching endlessly to the empty horizon, when there appear to be no streams at all in this seemingly timeless land.

Part of the answer may lie in the brief discussion in the immediately preceding section. Not all landforms in all deserts were necessarily formed under the climatic regime we see today; they may be fossil landscapes in a sense survivals of erosional patterns carved during a time more humid than ours. We shall see one result of a recent climatic shift a little further on when we talk about the Pleistocene (ice-age) lakes of the desert. Their abandoned shorelines contour the slopes of many of the mountains and their saline deposits whiten the floors of many of the western desert basins.

Not all the erosion of desert landscapes, however, was done in the remote geologic past and under climatic controls alien to the contemporary world. Almost all deserts have some rainfall, even though ten to fifteen years may elapse between showers.

Nature of the Run-Off

Contrary to popular belief, cloudbursts are relatively rare in arid lands—they are much more common where rainfall is greatest, as for example, the rainy tropics, or the southern Atlantic coastal states. When a moderate rain does fall on the desert, it is likely to assume the apparent proportions of a cloudburst in a more humid region and also to do a very effective job of erosion, because there is no vegetation to protect slopes from the spattering effect of rain drops, from rill wash, and from the rapid cutting of the ravines and arroyos that are so typical an aftermath of desert cloudbursts.

Anyone caught in one of these sudden downpours is likely to have an unforgettable experience should he fail to make his way to higher ground in a hurry. In a matter of moments, a dry sandy arroyo, bordered by low but steep cliffs, is filled with a surging, mud-laden flood. Such a stream swirls and churns forward violently, sweeping a great mass of debris along with it. Such flash floods make deserts impassable, until the arroyos drain. This they do almost as rapidly as they filled, because there is no continuing source of water supply for them as there is in regions of plentiful rain and perennial springs. In a matter of a few hours beneath the desert sun, an arroyo floor covered by 10 feet of water may be dry sand again, interrupted by only occasional pools of muddy water.

Such torrential floods as these short-lived desert ones may on occasion overtop the low banks of desert dry washes and spread out as a sheet of muddy, turbulent water over the desert floor. Such a *sheet flood* is vastly effective in picking up loose sediment and shifting it around the landscape.

Thus, deserts strike a curious balance when their rates of erosion are contrasted with those of humid regions. Much less rain falls in arid regions, but slopes are correspondingly more vulnerable because they lack the stabilizing effect of vegetation. Badlands, or slopes scored with great numbers of gullies, large and small, are characteristic desert landscape elements.

II

The Basin and Range Province of the Western United States

We have a broad desert of our own in western America, one well worth studying in its own right. Geologically it provides us with a superb sample of a desert environment and, although it might be more exciting to go to Tombouctou in the Sahara to study deserts, we can see almost every desert landform displayed in our own country. Only within recent years has the desert become a place to be visited instead of avoided. Now, for example, motels and swimming pools flourish where once dust-plumed wagon trains were targets for the Apache.

The mountainous landscapes of our own Southwest perhaps are not fully representative of the great deserts of the world—many of these are vast empty plains. Our desert possibly has more relief than most, and the mountain-girt bolson with a playa in its lowest part is a typical landform.

This alternation of mountains and basins was a most bewildering pattern for the pioneers. Since many of them came from more humid lands, most knew of the normally effective procedure when lost in well-watered lands, of walking down a stream valley until one came to a settlement, a lake, or the sea. In the American desert such a course of action more times than not led the wanderer to a barren sink with an alkali flat in its midst, across which the elusive mirage shimmered with its false promise of deliverance.

Lieutenant Colonel John C. Fremont had a reasonably sharp eye for terrain—especially when assisted by such redoubtable mountain men as Kit Carson. Fremont was one of the first to appreciate that the desert of eastern California, most of Nevada, and western Utah has an internal rather than external drainage, and a well-defined mountain rim partially encircling it—the Sierra Nevada to the west and the Wasatch to the east. Because of this unique geometry he coined the term *Great Basin* for the entire region. While the name is far from accurate, it is wonderfully descriptive and much more pictorial than the geologically more precise name of Basin and Range Province.

This last name does bring out the point that the Far West is a more mountainous realm than many other deserts of the world, and that these mountains are not linked together in such nearly continuous chains as the Alps and the Andes. Rather, the desert mountains rise as nearly separate islands above a sea of their own waste products.

The diagram (figure 6) of the characteristic features of the desert landscape, such as the bajada, pediment, and playa, is modeled on the typical terrain of the American Southwest. This is the landscape to be seen at Death Valley and in the vicinity of Las Vegas, as well as at such places as

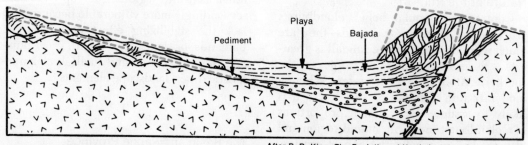

After P. B. King, *The Evolution of North America*. Copyright 1959. Reprinted by permission of Princeton University Press, Princeton, N. J.

Figure 6 *Diagram showing the characteristic features of a desert bolson in southwestern North America, with heavy dashed lines indicating the inferred size of mountain blocks prior to erosion.*

Reno and Salt Lake City. These desert mountains look curiously pale and bleached from the air, and their slopes, which are barren of vegetation, are deeply scored by ravines. The apices of alluvial fans head into every canyon and their radial streams may join at the base of the fan into a single trunk stream which leads to the playa. Time and again this pattern is repeated for the transcontinental traveler beating his way across the country. He may wonder at times why this region presents so corrugated an appearance, with isolated, narrow, nearly parallel mountain ranges alternating with broad, waste-filled depressions. He may take comfort in the fact that he is not alone in this wonderment, because geologists have speculated about the origin of these desert mountains for nearly a century without reaching a definitive answer.

. . . One of the hypotheses is that [mountains] owe their origin in part to faulting along their margins. Contributing support to this belief is the frequency of earthquakes in the western desert and the presence of scarps—many of them tens of feet high—which have appeared overnight as the result of displacement on active faults.

Desert Lakes

Whatever its origin, the alternation of mountains and basins of interior drainage in the Far West makes for unusual drainage patterns as contrasted to the more familiar terrain of well-watered regions. Among the many distinctive features of such a dry and furrowed landscape are the desert lakes. They owe their existence in large part to the inability of desert streams to develop through-flowing courses. Where such streams are blocked, even though by no more than the advancing toe of an alluvial fan, their water is ponded and a lake results. Some of these, such as Great Salt Lake with a surface area of about 2,000 square miles, are quite large.

Others are little more than saline ponds.

Almost all desert lakes have the common attribute that their water is brackish or saline to a greater or less degree. The concentration of salt in Great Salt Lake ranges from as little as 13 per cent to as much as 27 per cent of the weight of the water and is roughly four times greater than in the sea.

Desert lakes are extremely sensitive climatic indicators. In a dry cycle their water wastes away through evaporation and the drought-diminished streams are not able to hold their own against the loss. The lake level drops and the shores are bordered by an ever-widening band of salt. Most famous of such expanses is the Bonneville Salt Flat adjacent to Great Salt Lake, the scene of many a determined assault on land speed records.

Another interesting feature of deserts is the evidence that they were once the site of far larger lakes than the shrunken remnants that survive today. The most redoubtable of these now vanished inland seas in the United States was Lake Bonneville. This was the precursor of present-day Great Salt Lake, and shorelines of this one-time inland sea now scar the higher slopes of the Wasatch Mountains up to 1,000 feet above the modern lake. The area flooded by Lake Bonneville was close to 20,000 square miles, compared to the 2,000 or so of Great Salt Lake. During part of its history, Lake Bonneville had an outlet north to the Snake River and thence to the Pacific by way of the Columbia.

An interesting contemporary of Lake Bonneville was Lake Lahontan, located mostly in western Nevada not far from Reno. Since this is a strongly mountainous area today and all the intervening valleys were filled with long narrow arms of the lake the terrain pattern in some ways resembled the Norwegian fjords of today. Pyramid, Walker, and Winnemucca lakes are the chief surviving remnants of Lake Lahontan, but both Lahontan and Bonneville left their imprint on the landscape in an impressive array of wave-cut and wave-built landforms. Among these are wonderfully well-preserved beaches, gravel bars, sea cliffs, deltas, and limy tower-like deposits known as *tufa*. These last are built up underwater by lake-dwelling calcareous algae. In the arid climate of the western states these relics of a more humid time in the immediate geologic past are almost as perfectly preserved as though the lakes were in existence only yesterday. Radiocarbon dates indicate that indeed they were, since their lower levels were at the sills of caves occupied by human beings who lived there approximately 11,000 years ago.

A remarkable set of ice age lakes briefly was a part of the California landscape in the desert east of the Sierra Nevada. Individually these lakes, far smaller than such giants as Lahontan and Bonneville, were part of a whole system of connected lakes and streams. One series extended north from the site of modern Lake Arrowhead in the San Bernardino Mountains out across one of the driest of North American deserts to Death Valley. This now desiccated depression then held a lake perhaps 120 miles long and nearly 400 feet deep, to which the name Lake Manley is given. This honors the memory of Lewis Manley, a mountain man of tremendous strength and resolution, who saved the first party of pioneers to reach Death Valley. In a period of six weeks he hiked all the way to the coast and back again, and then back to the coast, in order to bring supplies and to lead the survivors out of their trap.

To the west of Death Valley a similar set of lakes and streams led from Mono Lake, at the base of the Sierra Nevada, down the length of Owens Valley to at least the basin of Searles Lake and possibly

U. S. Department of the Interior—National Park Serice Photo

Figure 7 Death Valley, California. The desert floor is the dry bed of an ancient lake.

on to Death Valley—although this last connection has not been positively demonstrated. At any rate, Searles Lake acted as a gigantic chemical processing plant, concentrating an enormous tonnage of dissolved material which is now being recovered from the dazzlingly white expanse of the saline playa.

The American desert has no monopoly on lakes, past and present, as they are equally characteristic of other arid regions throughout the world. Among well-known examples are Lake Chad in Africa, Lake Eyre in Australia, and Lop Nor, Lake Balkhash, and the Aral Sea in Central Asia. Not only were the Aral and Caspian seas larger in the recent geologic past than they are today, but they were connected with one another as well as with the Black Sea. Many others, such as the Dead Sea, are rimmed by abandoned shorelines that scar the barren slopes of the bordering desert hills much like gigantic flights of steps.

The obvious recency of these expanded lakes, coupled with the fact that their shorelines in a few favored locations, such as the flanks of the Wasatch and the Sierra Nevada, actually cut glacial moraines, leads many geologists to conclude that the last high stand of the lake coincided with the time of ice advance. The melt-water increase appears also to have been the cause of lake expansion, and as the glaciers of the world receded to their present diminished extent, the level of the desert lakes of North America fell. Many of them vanished almost entirely, leaving a barren expanse of salt or shrunken alkaline ponds as relics of what once was an inland sea.

Arid Erosion

. . . Many geologists believe that through combinations of downwasting and slope retreat a hilly or mountainous land may waste away until all that remains is a broad and featureless stripped plain nearly at sea level. Such a product of long-continued degradation . . . is called a peneplain.

Do peneplains form in deserts? At the moment the answer appears to be that no one really knows. There are many reasons for this ignorance. Among them is the fact that scientific investigation of deserts is a very recent activity. Almost all our experience with various kinds of erosion, with the operation of geologic processes, and with inferences as to their relative efficiency are derived from western Europe and the eastern United States. Both these regions have abundant precipitation with much of it falling as summer rain. Both as a rule have through-flowing streams, a nearly continuous mantle of vegetation, deep soil, and well-rounded hill slopes.

Yet the perplexing question remains with us that most of the landforms in deserts appear to have been shaped by running water, rather than, for example, by the wind.

The answer, at least in part, may be that much of what we see in a modern desert is in a sense a fossil landscape. A great deal of it may have been shaped by running water at a time when precipitation was greater than it is today. This is shown by the shorelines and other lake features which are (1) survivals of another climatic regime, and (2) preserved so well in a dry climate that they are an integral part of the present-day landscape.

Obviously this cannot be the sole explanation, because as we learned earlier it is a rare desert in which no rain ever falls. How effectively the resulting run-off erodes when compared to an equivalent amount in a humid region is debatable. Some believe more, some less, but all agree that some erosion does result. The truth is that far too little is known because we have so short a base line of experience from which to extrapolate with regard to the rates of erosive processes in deserts, or even relative efficacy of stream and wind abrasion.

Admitting, then, that stream erosion does operate in arid regions, it faces the peculiar limitation that many of the streams fail to reach the sea, and as a consequence of the resulting pattern of interior drainage the base level in each bolson rises. This is because debris washed down from the encircling hills has nowhere else to go and thus accumulates in the basin at the foot of the desert mountain range.

Streams which scar the flanks of these bordering hills are not idle either, and by eroding headward the more vigorous may succeed in cutting through a watershed separating two basins. Should this occur, the higher of the two troughs is very likely to be captured and the central playa as well as the tributary streams of the higher basin will then be diverted to the lower basin. Should this process of headward growth and capture continue long enough, then much of a desert region may have its drainage integrated and instead of having a multiple base level, with as many base levels as there are independent basins, the whole region will be tributary to the basin whose floor is at the lowest altitude.

This line of argument, although actually untested, seems reasonable enough for the early stages in the evolution of deserts with a ridge and basin topography resembling that of the Far West. How the level of an entire desert region is lowered, and how it can be reduced to a nearly level plain such as the broad expanses in the interior of Australia, are unanswered problems.

One of the questions at issue here is one that was raised earlier, and that is the possibility that some arid plains may have been shaped under a climatic regimen which is no longer operable. A time of greater rainfall and less local evaporation might be such a possibility. At any rate a leading modern view holds that many of these broad, stripped bedrock plains in the desert are the consequence of the gradual encroachment of pediments into the mountainous terrain at their heads. That is, as the pediments expand, the mountains are consumed and ultimately disappear. But in the final analysis the process of desert plain formation remains a mystery. So many are of such vast extent and the means available for their cutting seem so inadequate.

INDEX

A

absolute humidity, 58
Acapulco-Guatemala Trench, 32, 34, 35
adiabatic temperature change, 63
advection-radiation fog, 62
agricultural uses of water, 153-154
air, 48, 49, 116. *See also* atmosphere
Albatross, the, 104
Albertus Magnus, 149
al-Biruni,———,151
Aleutian Trench, 31, 32
altocumulus clouds, 66, 67
altostratus clouds, 66, 67
Anak Krakatoa, 93
Andaman Sea, 119
aquicludes, 164-166
aquifers, 164-166
Aquinas, Thomas, 149
Arabian Sea, 119
Aral Sea, 183
Arctic, 174
Arctic Ocean, 119
arid land, 173-174
Aristotle, on underground water, 149-150
Arrowhead, Lake, 182
artesian aquifers, 165-166
artesian wells, 148, 151
Artois and well construction, 148
Arx, William S. von, 112-114, 115-129, 130-
    144
Atacama Desert (South America), 176
Atlantic Ocean, 117
Atlantis, legend of, 95
Atlantis, the, 39
atmosphere, weight, 43; composition of, 43;
    functions, 44, 46; observation of, 48; con-
    stitution, 49; layers, 52-53; stability of, 64-
    65; as part of air, 116
atolls, 37-38
aurora borealis (northern lights), 48, 49

B

Baffin Bay (Greenland), 118

Balkhash, Lake (Central Asia), 183
Barents Sea, 119
Barnes, C. A., 134
baroclinic stratification, 139, 140
barotropic stratification, 139-140
Battan, Louis J., 73, 79
Bemmelen, van,———,92
Benguela current, 176
Bering Sea, 119
Bikini (atoll), 37
Bismarck Sea, 119
Black Sea, 183
bolometers, 46
Bonneville, Lake, 181, 182
Bradley, W. H., 97
Braham, R. R., Jr., 75
Bramlette, M. N., 97
Bretz, J. H., 152
Broecker, W. S., 98
Bullard, Sir Edward C., 106

C

caballing (of sea water), 136
cacti, 173
capillary fringe water, 162, 163
Capricorn Expedition (1953), 36-37
Caribbean Sea, 119
Carmel Canyon (California), 40
Cascade Mountains, 24
Caspian Sea, 133, 175, 183
Celebes Sea, 119
Chad, Lake, 183
Challenger, the, 95, 119, 125
Challenger Expedition (1872-1876), 96, 135
Charles Bal, the, 90-91
chemistry, and oceanography, 113-114
Chinese, and well drilling, 147
cirrocumulus clouds, 66, 67
cirrostratus clouds, 66, 67
cirrus clouds, 65, 66, 67
Clairault,———,129
Clarke, F. W., 119, 153
clouds, 65-67

coefficient of permeability, 160
coefficient of transmissibility, 160
condensation, 56, 60-64
consolidation of earth strata, 12
continental drift, 126
continental shelf, 38
continental slope, 38
convection cell hypothesis, 34, 35
convectional precipitation, 69
Cook, H.M.S., 33
coral islands, 37-38
Coral Sea, 119
coring, 96-97
Crater Lake (Oregon), 92, 93, (*il.* 94)
"Critias," Plato, 149
crust of the earth, 107-110
cryology, 146
cumulonimbus clouds, 66, 67

cyclones, 75, 76-78

D

Daly, R. A., 38, 123
Dana, J. D. 38
Darcy, Henry, 151, 152
Darwin, Charles, 38
Data of Geochemistry, The, Clarke, 119
Daubrée, A., 152
Davis, W. M., 38, 152
Dead Sea, 133, 175, 183
Death Valley (California), 180, 182, 183, (*il.* 24, 26, 182)
deep-well turbine pump, 148-149
depth of ocean, 125
deserts, misconception of, 171; locations, 172-174, 176; drainage, 175; kinds, 175; causes, 175-178; flash floods, 179; American, 180; mountains, 180-181; lakes, 181-183; fossil landscapes in, 183-184
dew, 61
De Wiest, Roger J. M., 145
diatom ooze, 100
diatrophism, 24

Dijon (France), 151
drought, 171, 172
"Du mouvement des eaux," Marotte, 151
Dupuit, Jules, 152
dust, 51
dust devils, 75, 76
Du Toit,——,152

E

earth, theory of origin, 14; composition, 116; mass and density, 126; shape, 127-129
Earth Beneath the Sea, The, Shepard, 96-111
Earth Science: The World We Live In, Namowitz and Stone, 48-53
East China Sea, 119
echo sounding, 29-31
effluent stream, 170
Egyptians, and well drilling, 147
Elements of Geography, Physical and Cultural, Finch, Trewartha, Robinson and Hammond, 55-72
Ellice Islands, 102
Emiliani, Cesare, 98
Eniwetok (atoll), 37
Eratosthenes, 127
Ericson, David, 98, 99
erosion, 123, 178-179
evaporation, 55
Ewing, John I., 106
Ewing, Maurice, 102, 105, 106
exosphere, 52
Explorer Expedition (1960), 28, 53
explosives, use on sea bottom, 105-106
Eyre, Lake, 183

F

Falcon Bank (island), 36-37
Fenner,——,120
Ferris, John G., 156

field capacity, 159

Finn. hydrogr.-biol. Unter-such., Witting, 135

fishing industry, and oceanography, 114

fluctuations of water level, 166-167

fog, 61-62

foraminifera, 100 (*il.* 98)

Forchheimer, Philip, 152

fracture zones, 35-36

Fremont, John C., 180

front, 71

G

Galathea Expedition (1950-1952), 137-138

Gamow, George, 42

Garden of the Gods (Colorado), 25, *il.* 26

geodesic, 129

geodesy, 129

geohydrology, defined, 145, 146; history 147-149; origin of subsurface water, 149-150; founders, 150-151; modern developments, 151-155

Geohydrology, De Wiest, 146-155

geoid, 129

geologic provinces (United States), 22

Geology, Putnam, 90-94, 172-184

Geology of Crater Lake National Park, Oregon, Williams, 92-93-94

geopotential surfaces, 129

Glacier Park (Montana), 25

Global Sea, The, Stewart, 29-41

globigerina ooze, 100

Goranson,——,120

gradation, 23

Grand Banks suspension flow, 124

gravitation, 127-129

gravity and the ocean basins, 110-111

Great Basin, 180

Great Salt Lake, 133, 161

"greenhouse effect," 44

ground water, 157-170

ground-water reservoir, 162-163

Gulf of Alaska, 31

Gulf of Bothnia, 124

Gulf of Mexico, 119

Guyot, Arnold, 37

guyots. *See* seamounts

H

Halley, Edmund, 119, 151

haloclines, 139

Hamilton, E. L., 107

Hawaiian Islands, 36, 152

heat capacity of sea water, 140-141

heat probe, 34

Helland-Hansen, Bjørn, 135

Hersey, J. Brackett, 106

Hill, Maurice N., 106

Horizon, the, 32, 33

horizontal convergence, 71

Hubbert, M. King, 153

Hudson canyon, 39

Humboldt Current, 176

humidity, 55, 58

Hunt, T. S., 153

Hutton, James, 10, 11-19, 120

hydrogeology. *See* hydrology

Hydrographical Tables, Knudsen, 134

hydrologic cycle, 56-57

hydrology, 146, 157-170

Hydrology, Wisler and Brater, 157-170

hydrosphere, 116

I

igneous activity, 24

Indian Ocean, 117, 129

industrial uses of water, 153-154

influent stream, 170

interior drainage of deserts, 175

internal water, 162

International Association of Scientific Hydrology (IASH), 146

International Ice Patrol, 134

interstitial water, 162

Introduction to Physical Geography, An,
   von Arx, 113-114, 116-129, 131-144
ionsphere, 50, 52

J

Jacob, C. E., 152
Japan Trench, 32
Java Sea, 119
Java Trench, 32, 33
jet stream, 84-88
Joly, John, 119

K

Kaijo Maru, 36
Kalahari Desert (Africa), 176
kanat system of water utilization, 148
Kara Sea, 119
Kennelly-Heaviside Layer, 52
Kepler, Johannes, 150
Kircher, Athanasius, 150
Knudsen, Martin, 134
Krakatoa, 90-94
Kuenen, P. H., 106, 124
Kullenberg, Börje, 96-97
Kulp, J. L., 98
Kurile-Kamchatka Trench, 32
Kusaba, General, 84

L

Lahontan, Lake, 181, 182
Lamont Geological Observatory (Columbia
   University), 35, 36, 98
latent heat of water vapor, 57
Laughton, A. R., 104
Leptus Magnus (Libya), 172
Lersch, B. M., 153
light absorption in water, 143
light penetration in sea water, 141-144
lithosphere, 116

limnology, 146
Loebsack, Theo, 83
Lop Nor (Central Asia), 183
Loran-C system of navigation, 30

M

Magnolia Petroleum Company, 103
main thermoclines, 139
manganese on ocean floor, 101, 102
Manley, Lake, 182
Manley, Lewis, 182
mantle of the earth, 107-108
marginal seas, 119
marginal sediment, 107
Mariannas Trench, 32, 33
marine geology, 28
Marine Geology, Kuenen, 106
Mariotte, Edmé, 150-151
Mazama, Mount, 93
McManus, R. P., 88
Mead, D., 146, 147
Mediterranean Sea, 119
Meinesz, Vening, 111
Meinzer, O. C., 146, 147, 152, 160
Mendocino Fault, 36
Meteor Expedition, 96
meteorology, 74
Mid-Atlantic Ridge, 35, 36
Middle Ages, 149
Mindanao (Philippine) Trench, 32, 33
Miojin Sho (Japan), 36
Moho. *See* Mohorovicic Discontinuity
Mohorovicic, A., 122
Mohorovicic Discontinuity, 107-109, 122
Mono Lake, 182
Monterey Submarine Canyon, 39-40
"Mundus Subterraneus," Kircher, 150
Muskat, Morris, 152-153, 160

N

Nafe, John, 104

Namowitz, Samuel N., 47
Nansei Shoto Trench, 32
Nature of Violent Storms, The, Battan, 74-78
New Britain Trench, 32, 33
New Hebrides, 32, 33
nimbostratus clouds, 66, 67

O

oceanic ridges, 35
oceanic trenches, 31-35
oceanography, 112-114
oceans, geometry of, 116-119; age, 119-120; origin, 120-121
ocean sediments, 96-101
Odell, Noel E., 25
oozes, 100
orographic precipitation, 70
Our Atmosphere, Loebsack, 84-88
ozone layer, 51

P

Pacific Ocean, 117
Palau Trench, 32, 33
Palissy, Bernard, 150
Pavlovsky, N. N., 153
peneplains, in deserts, 183
permeability of ground water, 160-162
permeameters, 160-161
Perrault, Pierre, 150-151
Peru-Chile Trench, 32
Petterson, Hans, 104
Philippine Trench. *See* Mindanao Trench
piezometric surface, 164
Piggot, Charles, 96
Planet Called Earth, A, Gamow, 43-46
plankton, 100
Plato, on underground water, 149
playas (dry lakes), 175
Playfair, John, 120
Polubarinova Kochina, P. Ya., 153

porosity of rocks, 158
potamology, 146
precipitation, 54, 56, 57, 68-72
Putnam, William C., 89-94, 171-184
pycnoclines, 139
Pyramid Lake, 181

R

radar, 81-82
Radar Observes the Weather, Battan, 80-82
radiation (ground-inversion) fog, 61
Radiolaria, 102
rain, 68. *See also* precipitation
rain shadow, 70
Raitt, Russell W., 106, 109, 110
red clays, 100-101
refraction method of ocean exploring, 105-106
relative humidity, 58-60
Revelle, Roger, 107
Rex, Robert, 101
Riedel, W. R., 102
"ring of fire," 33
Roman aquaduct system, 145
Ross Sea, 117
rotary drilling, 148

S

salt content of seas, 119-120
Salton Sea, 133
saturation, 59
Scarborough (England), 152
Scheuchzer, Johann, 151
Schleicher-Bradshaw salinometer, 134-135
Scotia Sea, 119
Scripps Canyon (California), 40
Scripps Institution of Oceanography, 32, 35, 37
Sculptured Earth, The, Shimer, 21-27
seamounts (guyots), 30-31, 36-37, 101-102 (*il.* 101)

Sea of Japan, 119
Sea of Okhotsk, 119
Searles Lake, 182, 183
seasonal thermoclines, 139
sea water, composition, 114; characteristics, 130-144; density, 131-132; salinity, 132-135; elements in, 133; chlorinity, 134; temperature-salinity relationship, 135-137; adiabatic effects, 137-139; stratification, 139-140; heat capacity, 140-141; light penetration, 141-144
sediment thickness, 106-107
seepage, 169-170
Seine River, 151
Selin-Bekchurin,——,153
Seneca, Lucius Annaeus, 150
sheet flood, 179
Shepard, Francis P., 95
Shimer, John A., 20, 21-27
Shor, George, 109
Shumway, G. A., 104
Sierra Nevada Mountains, 176, 183
Slichter, C. A., 152
Smith, William, 152
Snellius Expedition, 96
Snell's law of refraction, 138, 142
soil water, 162, 163
Sonoprobe, 103-104
Soule, F. M., 134
South China Sea, 119
specific humidity, 58
specific retention of ground water, 159
specific yield of ground water, 159-160
Spindle Top oil field, 148
squall zones, 87, 88
Stabler, Herman, 153
Stearns, H. T., 152
steppe, 173
Stewart, Harris B., 28
Stone, Donald B., 47
stratification of sea water, 139-140
stratocumulus clouds, 66, 67
stratopause, 50, 52
stratosphere, 44, 50, 52
stratus clouds, 66, 67

submarine canyons, 39-40
subsurface (ground) water. *See* geohydrology
subterranean hydrology. *See* geohydrology
Sunset Crater (Arizona), 24, 25 (*il.* 25)

T

Tasman Sea, 119
Telegraph Plateau, 124
temperature-salinity diagram, 135-136
temple of Serapis, 24
terrigenous muds, 101
Thales, 149
Theis, C. V., 152, 160
thermoclines, 139
Theory of the Earth, Hutton, 11-19
thickness of ocean sediment, 106-107
Thiem, Adolph, 152
Tonga-Kermadec Trench, 32, 33
tornadoes, 75, 76
trade winds, 176
transmissibility, 160
Trieste, the, 32
Tropic of Cancer, 175
Tropic of Capricorn, 175
tropopause, 50, 52
troposphere, 43, 50, 52
tufa, 182
turbidity current, 124

U

underflow, 169
uniformitarianism, 93, 120
U. S. Coast and Geodetic Survey, 31, 40
Urey, Harold, 98

V

vadose water, 162
Vallisnieri, Antonio, 151

Vine, Allyn C., 105
Vitruvius, Marcus, 150
Vityaz, the, 33
volcanism, 89
volcanoes, location of, 121

W

Walker Lake, 181
Wasatch Mountains, 181, 183
water table, 163-165
water vapor, 51, 55, 57
Weber, Herman, 152
Weber Trough, 32, 33
Weddell Sea, 117, 119
Weibull, W., 104
wells and well construction in ancient
    times, 147-148
Wenner, F., 134
Wenner bridge, 134, 135
Wenzel, L. K., 160
white frost, 61

Williams, Howel, 92
wind systems, 75
Winnemucca Lake, 181
Wister, Chester Owen, and E. F. Brater,
    Hydrology, 157-170
Witting, R., 135
Woodcock,——,119
Woollard, George P., 105
world ocean, 117
Worzel, J. Lamar, 105, 111

X

xerophyte, 173

Z

Zies, E. G., 120
zone of aeration, 162, 163
zone of saturation, 162, 163
zones of water storage, 162-163